DEFENSE, SECURITY AND STRATEGIES

NATIONAL EMERGENCY COMMUNICATIONS PLAN

COMPONENTS AND CHALLENGES

DEFENSE, SECURITY AND STRATEGIES

Additional books in this series can be found on Nova's website
under the Series tab.

Additional e-books in this series can be found on Nova's website
under the e-book tab.

DEFENSE, SECURITY AND STRATEGIES

NATIONAL EMERGENCY COMMUNICATIONS PLAN

COMPONENTS AND CHALLENGES

CARL R. BUSH
EDITOR

nova publishers
New York

Library of Congress Cataloging-in-Publication Data

ISBN: 978-1-63463-899-9

Published by Nova Science Publishers, Inc. † *New York*

CONTENTS

Preface   vii

Chapter 1 National Emergency Communications Plan   1
               U.S. Department of Homeland Security

Chapter 2 The First Responder Network (FirstNet) and
               Next-Generation Communications for Public Safety:
               Issues for Congress   127
               Linda K. Moore

Index   163

PREFACE

This book discusses the components and challenges of the National Emergency Communications Plan.

Chapter 1 - The National Emergency Communications Plan (NECP) is the Nation's over-arching strategic plan for enhancing emergency communications capabilities and interoperability nationwide. The NECP updates the original plan issued in 2008 and addresses the increasingly complex communications landscape that the public safety community uses to keep America safe and secure. The plan provides a roadmap for improving emergency communications for traditional emergency responder disciplines such as law enforcement, fire, and emergency medical services, while recognizing the importance of engaging non-traditional disciplines including public health, public works and transportation agencies.

Chapter 2 - Since September 11, 2001, when communications failures contributed to the tragedies of the day, Congress has passed several laws intended to create a nationwide emergency communications capability. Yet the United States has continued to strive for a solution that assures seamless communications among first responders and emergency personnel at the scene of a major disaster. To address this problem, Congress included provisions in the Middle Class Tax Relief and Job Creation Act of 2012 (P.L. 112-96) for planning, building, and managing a new, nationwide, broadband network for public safety communications (FirstNet), and assigned additional radio frequency spectrum to accommodate the new network. In addition, the act has designated federal appropriations of over $7 billion for the network and other public safety needs. These funds will be provided through new revenue from the auction of spectrum licenses. These and other public safety and spectrum provisions of the act appear in Title VI, known as the Public Safety and Spectrum Act, or Spectrum Act.

There are many challenges for public safety leaders and policy makers in establishing the framework for a nationwide network that meets state, local, and tribal needs for robust, interoperable emergency communications. For example, emergency communications networks currently operate on separate networks using different technologies. Because public safety planning has lagged behind commercial efforts to build next-generation wireless networks, the work on design and development of technical requirements for a public safety broadband network is incomplete. Furthermore, each state has its own laws and procedures for building, managing, and funding its network. Establishing a governance model that accommodates current investments and future needs without compromising the coherence of a national network is another challenge. The cost of construction of a nationwide network for public safety is estimated by experts to be in the tens of billions of dollars over the long term, with similarly large sums needed for maintenance and operation. In expectation that private sector participation in building the new network will reduce costs to the public sector, the law has provided some requirements and guidelines for partnerships, access to spectrum, and shared use of infrastructure. Identifying and negotiating with potential partners is another challenge for the new network, as is establishing a revenue stream to fund operations and future investments.

These and other challenges are potential barriers to the success of the new network. To meet them in a timely manner may require significant investments in human resources in the early stages of the network. Therefore, yet another challenge to success may arise from federal hiring requirements and the release of funds to cover salaries and expenses while FirstNet is in start-up mode.

In addition to monitoring progress in building the new broadband network for public safety, Congress may want to consider reviewing the role of commercial networks in emergency response and recovery. Once commercial communications lines are compromised because of infrastructure failures, interdependent public safety networks are threatened and the ability to communicate vital information to the public is diminished. New policy initiatives may be needed to identify critical gaps in communications infrastructure and the means to fund the investments needed to close these gaps.

In: National Emergency Communications Plan   ISBN: 978-1-63463-899-9
Editor: Carl R. Bush   © 2015 Nova Science Publishers, Inc.

Chapter 1

NATIONAL EMERGENCY COMMUNICATIONS PLAN[*]

U.S. Department of Homeland Security

2014 GOALS AND RECOMMENDATIONS

GOAL 1 – GOVERNANCE AND LEADERSHIP: *Enhance decision-making, coordination, and planning for emergency communications through strong governance structures and leadership.*

Recommendations:

- Update governance structures and processes to address the evolving operating environment.
- Increase intra-State collaboration of communications, broadband, and information technology activities.
- Increase regional structures or processes to foster multi-State coordination and information sharing.
- Enable the Emergency Communications Preparedness Center to serve as the Federal focal point for coordination with the First Responder Network Authority.

---

[*] This is an edited, reformatted and augmented version of a document issued November 2014.

- Increase coordination of public safety and national security and emergency preparedness communications requirements and policies.
- Promote opportunities to share Federal emergency communications infrastructure and resources.
- Promote consistent policies across Federal grant programs and investments.
- Improve the ability to assess the impact of emergency communications grant funding.

GOAL 2 – PLANNING AND PROCEDURES: *Update plans and procedures to improve emergency responder communications and readiness in a dynamic operating environment.*

Recommendations:

- Update Statewide Communications Interoperability Plans to maintain Land Mobile Radio systems and address wireless broadband deployments.
- Coordinate Federal strategic planning for broadband capabilities through the Emergency Communications Preparedness Center.
- Enable One DHS to lead the implementation of a DHS strategic plan for emergency communications.
- Ensure nationwide public safety broadband planning is coordinated throughout each State and territory and focuses on responders' current and future needs.
- Establish points of contact to coordinate Federal broadband planning and deployment activities.
- Expand lifecycle planning activities to address broadband deployments and security, as needed.
- Evaluate, update, and distribute standard operating procedures to address new technologies and align them to tactical plans.
- Ensure standard operating procedures reflect current use of priority telecommunications services.
- Coordinate with entities from across the broader emergency response community to develop communications standard operating procedures.

GOAL 3 – TRAINING AND EXERCISES: *Improve responders' ability to coordinate and communicate through training and exercise programs that* *use all available technologies and target gaps in emergency communications.*

Recommendations:

- Develop training and exercise programs that target gaps in emergency communications capabilities and use new technologies.
- Identify opportunities to integrate more private and public sector communications stakeholders into training and exercises.
- Increase responder proficiency with Federal and national interoperability channels through training and exercises.
- Use regional governance structures to develop and promote training and exercise opportunities.
- Leverage technologies, conferences, and workshops to increase training and exercise opportunities.
- Promote awareness of and cross-training among Federal, State, local, tribal, and territorial Incident Command System Communications Unit personnel through training and exercises.
- Develop and share best practices on processes to recognize trained Communications Unit personnel.
- Improve States' and territories' ability to track and share trained Communications Unit personnel during response operations.

GOAL 4 – OPERATIONAL COORDINATION: *Ensure operational effectiveness through the coordination of emergency communications capabilities, resources, and personnel from across the whole community.*

Recommendations:

- Ensure inventories of emergency communication resources are updated and comprehensive.
- Enhance jurisdictions' ability to readily request communications resources or assets during operations.
- Implement Incident Command System communications-related roles, responsibilities, and planning.
- Ensure operational planning incorporates new technologies and communications partners.

- Ensure Public Safety Answering Point and Public Safety Communications Center continuity of operations planning addresses systems and staffing to support dispatch communications.
- Update procedures for implementing backup communications solutions.
- Increase Federal departments' and agencies' preparation and support for local emergency communications needs.

GOAL 5 – RESEARCH AND DEVELOPMENT: *Coordinate research, development, testing, and evaluation activities to develop innovative emergency communications capabilities that support the needs of emergency responders.*

Recommendations:

- Coordinate Federal research and development priorities and user requirements through the Emergency Communications Preparedness Center.
- Increase collaboration between Federal research and development and technology transfer programs across the homeland security, defense, and national security communities.
- Foster collaborative mission critical voice, data, and cybersecurity research, development, testing and evaluation.
- Government research facilities should facilitate the integration of Next Generation 9-1-1 into a nationwide solution.
- Cultivate an innovative marketplace for applications and technologies through the use of public and private partnerships.
- Support the evolution of alert and warning systems that deliver timely, relevant, and accessible emergency information to the public.
- Update priority service programs to successfully migrate to internet protocol-enabled fixed and mobile broadband networks.
- Increase use and awareness of the Project 25 Compliance Assessment Program.
- Continue to support Project 25 standards development for interoperability.

EXECUTIVE SUMMARY

In 2008, the Department of Homeland Security (DHS) published the *National Emergency Communications Plan* (or the Plan) to accelerate improvements for public safety communications nationwide. Title XVIII of the *Homeland Security Act of 2002*, as amended, directs the DHS Office of Emergency Communications to develop and periodically update the National Emergency Communications Plan in coordination with Federal, State, local, tribal, territorial, and private sector stakeholders.[1] The law also directs the Plan to set benchmarks for enhancing emergency communications capabilities and for the Office of Emergency Communications to measure progress toward achieving those milestones.

> The National Emergency Communications Plan is a strategic national emergency communications plan that promotes communication and sharing of information across all levels of government, jurisdictions, disciplines, and organizations for all threats and hazards, as needed and when authorized.

The emergency communications landscape has evolved into a new, complex operating environment since the release of the 2008 National Emergency Communications Plan. Among the key developments are major changes in policy, legislation, budget conditions, and communications technologies. This includes the establishment of the First Responder Network Authority, which is charged with ensuring the building, deployment, and operation of a Nationwide Public Safety Broadband Network.

To prepare stakeholders for this dynamic environment, the Office of Emergency Communications led a national effort to update the National Emergency Communications Plan to account for new technologies for emergency responders. This Plan also addresses the necessity of Land Mobile Radio systems for ensuring the availability of mission critical voice capabilities.

The Office of Emergency Communications conducted outreach to more than 350 stakeholders involved in emergency communications to develop this version of the National Emergency Communications Plan. This included representatives from all major public safety organizations; emergency management agencies; Federal, State, local, tribal, and territorial governments; the private sector; and other emergency response agencies or entities such as utilities, nongovernmental organizations, and auxiliary resources.

Leveraging the foundation established by the 2008 National Emergency Communications Plan, this Plan aims to improve the key communications capabilities of emergency responders at all levels of government—notably the policies, governance structures, planning, and protocols that enable them to communicate and share information under all circumstances. The National Emergency Communications Plan's top priorities for the next three to five years are:

- Identifying and prioritizing areas for improvement in emergency responders' Land Mobile Radio systems;
- Ensuring emergency responders and government officials plan and prepare for the adoption, integration, and use of broadband technologies, including the planning and deployment of the Nationwide Public Safety Broadband Network; and
- Enhancing coordination among stakeholders, processes, and planning activities across the emergency response community.

To achieve these priorities, the Office of Emergency Communications has centered the National Emergency Communications Plan around five goals that provide continuity with the first national plan and align to the *SAFECOM Interoperability Continuum*.[2] The National Emergency Communications Plan goals are strategic in nature and aim to enhance emergency communications capabilities at all levels of government in coordination with the private sector, nongovernmental organizations, and communities across the Nation. The five National Emergency Communications Plan goals are:

- **Goal 1 - Governance and Leadership:** Enhance decision-making, coordination, and planning for emergency communications through strong governance structures and leadership
- **Goal 2 - Planning and Procedures:** Update plans and procedures to improve emergency responder communications and readiness in a dynamic operating environment

- **Goal 3 - Training and Exercises:** Improve responders' ability to coordinate and communicate through training and exercise programs that use all available technologies and target gaps in emergency communications
- **Goal 4 - Operational Coordination:** Ensure operational effectiveness through the coordination of communications capabilities, resources, and personnel from across the whole community
- **Goal 5 - Research and Development:** Coordinate research, development, testing, and evaluation activities to develop innovative emergency communications capabilities that support the needs of emergency responders

To implement the 2014 National Emergency Communications Plan, the Office of Emergency Communications will coordinate with public safety agencies and emergency responders from across the Nation through partnerships such as the SAFECOM Executive Committee/Emergency Response Council, the Emergency Communications Preparedness Center, and the National Council of Statewide Interoperability Coordinators, among others. Together, DHS and its partners will identify strategies and timelines to accomplish the Plan's goals, objectives, and recommendations and measure progress nationwide. The National Emergency Communications Plan's results will help DHS and Federal, State, local, tribal, and territorial stakeholders target their resources for emergency communications, including training, technical assistance, planning, outreach, and response and recovery operations.

The future of emergency communications is at a critical juncture. Through the National Emergency Communications Plan and the work of the Office of Emergency Communications and its partners, DHS is committed to ensuring that our Nation's emergency responders can meet their mission needs and achieve the long-term vision of the Plan:

To enable the Nation's emergency response community to communicate and share information across levels of government, jurisdictions, disciplines, and organizations for all threats and hazards, as needed and when authorized

> **National Emergency Communications Plan Vision**
> To enable the Nation's emergency response community to communicate and share information across levels of government, jurisdictions, disciplines, and organizations for all threats and hazards, as needed and when authorized

1.0. INTRODUCTION

The Nation's preparedness and resilience continue to be tested by emergencies and disasters of varying scope and magnitude. This includes natural disasters that stretch across jurisdictional borders, such as hurricanes, earthquakes, and tornados; active shooter incidents in both large and small communities; and individual and terrorists' attempts to disrupt the safety and security of the American people, including the 2013 Boston Marathon bombings. These and other emergencies are stark reminders that our Nation must be ready to respond to all types of threats and hazards—whether natural, technological, or man-made.

Since the Department of Homeland Security's (DHS) establishment in 2003, one of its top priorities has been to improve the communications capabilities of those who are often the first to arrive at the scene of an incident: the Nation's emergency responders. DHS has partnered with the emergency response community to ensure that law enforcement, fire, and emergency medical services personnel have access to reliable and interoperable communications at all times in order to save lives, protect property and the environment, stabilize communities, and meet basic human needs following an incident.[3] This relationship reflects the fact that a government-centric approach is not sufficient to meet the challenges posed by today's threats and hazards.[4]

> **Emergency Communications**
>
> The means and methods for exchanging communications and information necessary for successful incident management.

Title XVIII of the *Homeland Security Act of 2002* provided renewed focus and vitality to this critical homeland security mission.[5] The legislation established the DHS Office of Emergency Communications to lead the development and implementation of a comprehensive national approach to advance national interoperable communications capabilities. To achieve this objective, the Act also required DHS to develop the *National Emergency Communications Plan* (or the Plan).[6]

As the Nation's first strategic plan for emergency communications, the National Emergency Communications Plan established a vision for emergency responders at all levels of government to strive to achieve: ensuring the availability of communications as needed, on demand, and as authorized across all disciplines and jurisdictions. To achieve this vision, the Plan approached interoperability as a critical capability that must be developed and enhanced through partnerships, ongoing training, and joint planning and investments at all levels of government.

> **Statutory Requirements**
> The Homeland Security Act of 2002 (6 United States Code § 572) requires Department of Homeland Security (DHS) to establish and periodically update the National Emergency Communications Plan in cooperation with State, local, and tribal governments, Federal departments and agencies, emergency response providers, and the private sector and "provide recommendations regarding how the United States should support and promote the ability of emergency response providers and relevant government officials to continue to communicate in the event of disasters and to ensure, accelerate, and attain interoperable emergency communications nationwide." For more information on how the National Emergency Communications Plan meets the statutory requirements in 6 United States Code § 572, refer to Appendix 1.

Since the release of the first National Emergency Communications Plan in 2008, several technological, policy, and other developments have directly impacted emergency communications. One key development is the Nationwide Public Safety Broadband Network, which will be deployed using wireless Internet Protocol-based technologies. The Nationwide Public Safety

Broadband Network will transform how emergency responders communicate and share information by increasing the availability of wireless broadband access and innovative mobile applications to public safety personnel nationwide.

In addition to technological developments, new policies provide direction for Federal departments and agencies on critical issues such as National Security and Emergency Preparedness communications.[7] Simultaneously, the Nation is evolving its approach to preparing for and responding to incidents through the *National Preparedness Goal*, which promotes a shared responsibility across all levels of government, private and nonprofit sectors, and the general public. DHS is also partnering with public and private sector stakeholders to improve the cybersecurity and resiliency of the Nation's critical infrastructure, including telecommunications networks and emergency services.[8] The *National Infrastructure Protection Plan 2013: Partnering for Critical Infrastructure Security and Resilience* guides the national effort to manage risk to the Nation's critical infrastructure.

Further, although natural phenomena such as hurricanes and other extreme weather events are not new hazards, trends in the frequency and severity of such events have increased their impact on the Nation. The DHS 2014 *Quadrennial Homeland Security Review* identifies evolving threats from natural disasters as having major implications for national preparedness and resilience, including emergency communications.[9]

1.1. Purpose

In light of this changing environment, the Office of Emergency Communications led a national effort to develop a new National Emergency Communications Plan. The focus of this Plan is to ensure that strategies, resource decisions, and investments for emergency communications keep pace with the evolving environment, and that the emergency response community is collectively driving toward a common end-state for communications.

This version builds on the framework established by the 2008 National Emergency Communications Plan to enhance the key communications capabilities of emergency responders at all levels of government— notably the policies, governance structures, and planning and protocols that support their ability to communicate and share information under all circumstances.[10]

To develop the 2014 Plan, the Office of Emergency Communications used an extensive outreach process, involving more than 350 stakeholders, to identify the key challenges facing emergency communications and propose solutions to address them. The Office of Emergency Communications considered input from representatives from all major public safety organizations; Federal, State, local, tribal, and territorial governments; and key private sector partners, such as the communications and information technology sectors. They recommended updating the Plan's vision, goals, and objectives to reflect emergency responders' increasing use of data and video services during operations, as well as the continued need to maintain or upgrade their Land Mobile Radio mission critical voice communications capabilities.

To that end, the National Emergency Communications Plan identifies three top priorities for emergency communications over the next three to five years:

- Identifying and prioritizing areas for improvement in emergency responders' Land Mobile Radio systems;
- Ensuring emergency responders and government officials plan and prepare for the adoption, integration, and use of broadband technologies, including the planning and deployment of the Nationwide Public Safety Broadband Network; and
- Enhancing coordination among stakeholders, processes, and planning activities across the emergency response community.

1.2. Scope

The National Emergency Communications Plan is a plan for the Nation. It provides information and guidance to those that plan for, coordinate, invest in, and use communications to support response and recovery operations. This includes traditional emergency responder disciplines (e.g., fire, law enforcement, emergency medical services), other entities that need to communicate and share information during emergencies, such as public health and medical, public works, and transportation agencies, as well as appointed and elected officials. The Plan is also designed for Federal, State, local, tribal, and territorial governmental personnel who are responsible for setting mission priorities, developing budgets, and planning for and acquiring communications technology assets.

In addition, the National Emergency Communications Plan seeks to increase coordination and planning with the growing number of entities that communicate and share information with public safety personnel and organizations during emergencies, including the public and other emergency response agencies or entities such as utilities, nongovernmental organizations, international partners, auxiliary resources, and commercial service providers.[11] In addition to interoperability, the Plan also provides recommendations to ensure that emergency response providers and relevant government officials (e.g., Federal Executive Branch, State, local, tribal, and territorial officials) can continue to communicate in the event of disasters and acts of terrorism.[12]

1.3. Progress

The 2014 National Emergency Communications Plan builds upon the progress and lessons learned from implementing the 2008 Plan. As part of its legislative requirements, the Plan established a baseline level of interoperability and set timeframes for jurisdictions to achieve the baseline. Through the 2008 National Emergency Communications Plan goals, the Office of Emergency Communications measured communications capabilities throughout all 56 States and territories. More than 90 percent of the 2008 Plan's milestones to enhance emergency communications capabilities were achieved, and the Nation's jurisdictions collectively demonstrated the Plan's performance-based goals.[13]

Further, in addition to successfully meeting the Plan's requirements, the National Emergency Communications Plan improved key foundational elements for effective emergency communications. For example, as a result of the 2008 National Emergency Communications Plan, dozens of new governance structures and leadership positions were established at the State and territorial levels to coordinate planning and decision-making for interoperability and broadband deployment. In addition, hundreds of local public safety agencies have developed tactical plans and protocols to coordinate communications during emergencies, and several thousand responders and technicians have been trained to lead communications during incidents across the Nation.

1.4. Organization of the National Emergency Communications Plan

The 2014 Plan supersedes the 2008 National Emergency Communications Plan and is effective immediately. The framework of the National Emergency Communications Plan is organized as follows:

- **Section 2.0 – Emergency Communications Landscape.** This section provides an overview of the evolving operating environment, including key technological developments, and provides background for the Plan's priorities, goals, and recommendations.
- **Section 3.0 – National Emergency Communications Plan Strategic Components.** This section, as depicted in Exhibit 1, establishes the strategy to meet the Plan's priorities and better position the emergency response community for the current and evolving communications operating environment.
- **Section 4.0 – Implementation and Measurement.** This section describes the approach for measuring and assessing progress toward implementing the National Emergency Communications Plan and improving emergency communications capabilities at all levels of government, and across disciplines, nationwide.

2.0. EMERGENCY COMMUNICATIONS LANDSCAPE

The emergency communications landscape has changed significantly since publication of the 2008 National Emergency Communications Plan. At that time, Land Mobile Radio systems were—and still are—the primary means for emergency responders to achieve mission critical voice communications. Public safety was in the early stages of adopting broadband and mobile data services, and the deployment of a nationwide public safety network was a notional concept. As a result, the 2008 National Emergency Communications Plan goals and priorities were largely focused around building the plans, processes, and structures to enhance Land Mobile Radio operability, interoperability, and continuity.

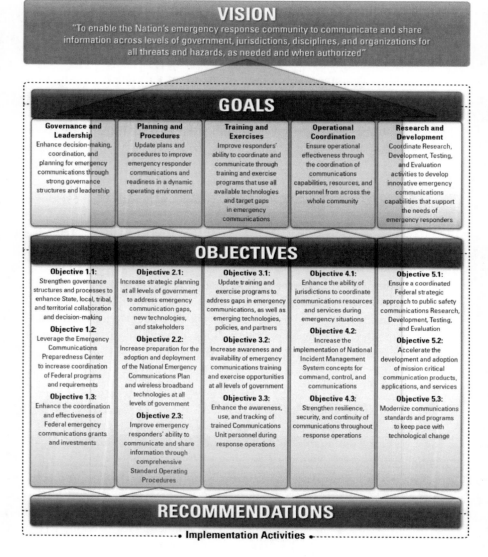

VISION

"To enable the Nation's emergency response community to communicate and share information across levels of government, jurisdictions, disciplines, and organizations for all threats and hazards, as needed and when authorized"

GOALS

Governance and Leadership	Planning and Procedures	Training and Exercises	Operational Coordination	Research and Development
Enhance decision-making, coordination, and planning for emergency communications through strong governance structures and leadership	Update plans and procedures to improve emergency responder communications and readiness in a dynamic operating environment	Improve responders' ability to coordinate and communicate through training and exercise programs that use all available technologies and target gaps in emergency communications	Ensure operational effectiveness through the coordination of communications capabilities, resources, and personnel from across the whole community	Coordinate Research, Development, Testing, and Evaluation activities to develop innovative emergency communications capabilities that support the needs of emergency responders

OBJECTIVES

Objective 1.1: Strengthen governance structures and processes to enhance State, local, tribal, and territorial collaboration and decision-making	**Objective 2.1:** Increase strategic planning at all levels of government to address emergency communication gaps, new technologies, and stakeholders	**Objective 3.1:** Update training and exercise programs to address gaps in emergency communications, as well as emerging technologies, policies, and partners	**Objective 4.1:** Enhance the ability of jurisdictions to coordinate communications resources and services during emergency situations	**Objective 5.1:** Ensure a coordinated Federal strategic approach to public safety communications Research, Development, Testing, and Evaluation
Objective 1.2: Leverage the Emergency Communications Preparedness Center to increase coordination of Federal programs and requirements	**Objective 2.2:** Increase preparation for the adoption and deployment of the National Emergency Communications Plan and wireless broadband technologies at all levels of government	**Objective 3.2:** Increase awareness and availability of emergency communications training and exercise opportunities at all levels of government	**Objective 4.2:** Increase the implementation of National Incident Management System concepts for command, control, and communications	**Objective 5.2:** Accelerate the development and adoption of mission critical communication products, applications, and services
Objective 1.3: Enhance the coordination and effectiveness of Federal emergency communications grants and investments	**Objective 2.3:** Improve emergency responders' ability to communicate and share information through comprehensive Standard Operating Procedures	**Objective 3.3:** Enhance the awareness, use, and tracking of trained Communications Unit personnel during response operations	**Objective 4.3:** Strengthen resilience, security, and continuity of communications throughout response operations	**Objective 5.3:** Modernize communications standards and programs to keep pace with technological change

RECOMMENDATIONS

• Implementation Activities •

Exhibit 1. The National Emergency Communications Plan Strategy.

In recent years, a more complex and interdependent landscape has emerged due to new technologies, policies, and stakeholders involved in emergency communications. Land Mobile Radio systems delivering mission critical voice communications remain an integral component of the landscape;

however, emergency responders are using more mobile data services and applications to share information and augment their mission critical voice capabilities.

> **Involving the Whole Community**
>
> The whole community concept, which is the underlying principle of Presidential Policy Directive 8 and the National Preparedness Goal, is a means by which individuals, emergency management practitioners, organizational and community leaders, and government officials can collectively understand and assess the needs of their respective communities and determine the best ways to organize and strengthen their assets, capacities, and interests.

In addition, response agencies are becoming more connected to other entities that need to communicate and share information during emergencies, such as public health, medical, and transportation agencies, critical infrastructure sectors (e.g., Energy, Information Technology, and others), and the public. While individuals in these entities are not always trained response personnel, they can help share valuable information and provide situational awareness during response and recovery efforts. This can be attributed to technology advancements, such as the widespread use of social media during emergencies, as well as new national preparedness doctrine that underscores the importance of engaging the whole community during emergencies.[14]

Moreover, information security and privacy considerations also shape the operating environment. The increasing availability of data and information essential to emergency communications operations and related technologies has both fundamentally changed and enabled more efficient and effective practices. This information is vulnerable to unauthorized access that could affect its confidentiality, integrity, or availability. It is critical to coordinate on security and privacy issues, as well as the management of sensitive data, while maintaining the availability and distribution of information for those who need it; this entails being transparent about information-sharing practices; protecting sources and methods; and ensuring privacy[15] and protecting civil liberties, while also enabling law enforcement investigations. This section addresses how the convergence of people, processes, and technologies is transforming the emergency communications landscape now and into the future.

2.1. Land Mobile Radio and Wireless Broadband Infrastructure

For nearly a century, the public safety community has used Land Mobile Radio networks for reliable, instantaneous, two-way voice communications. Land Mobile Radio systems are designed to meet emergency responders' unique mission critical requirements and support time-sensitive, lifesaving tasks, including rapid voice call-setup, group calling capabilities, high-quality audio, and guaranteed priority access to the end-user. Because these radio systems support lifesaving operations, they are designed to achieve high levels of reliability, redundancy, coverage, and capacity, and can operate in harsh natural and man-made environments. Land Mobile Radio technology has progressed over time from conventional analog voice service to complex systems incorporating digital and trunking features. These enhancements have improved the security, reliability, and functionality of voice communications.

For the foreseeable future, the public safety community is expected to follow a multi-path approach to network infrastructure use and development. Land Mobile Radio systems will remain the primary tool for mission critical voice communications for many years to come; in fact, for many public safety agencies, maintaining their Land Mobile Radio systems and improving operability and interoperability continue to be their top communications priorities.

To augment their Land Mobile Radio capabilities, emergency response agencies are increasingly using commercial wireless broadband services and, in some cases, procuring private broadband networks with faster data capabilities. Although commercial broadband networks do not meet public safety's unique requirements for mission critical voice communications, they can provide a range of data capabilities that enhance operational efficiency.

Broadband networks, particularly the Nationwide Public Safety Broadband Network, stand to transform how emergency responders will communicate by providing unparalleled connectivity and bandwidth that enhance situational awareness and information sharing. Moreover, the Nationwide Public Safety Broadband Network will offer emergency responders benefits that are not available using only commercial systems, including the ability to provide coverage of underserved geographic areas and the ability to prioritize bandwidth allocations for public safety use, especially during catastrophic incidents.

The emergency response community's adoption of broadband capabilities is likely to occur in phases over several years. The pace will vary among agencies and jurisdictions depending on the requirements of the local operating environment, the lifecycle of current communications systems, and funding levels. As the public safety community integrates broadband into its emergency communications operations, a number of challenges will need to be addressed at all levels of government. These challenges will involve not only technology but, much like Land Mobile Radio, will also involve governance, standard operating procedures, training, and sustainable investments.

2.2. Broadband Applications and Services

The move toward a wireless broadband infrastructure will provide the means to transfer large amounts of data almost anywhere, at any time, at much faster rates than those available today. Similar to the commercial Internet, this high-bandwidth connectivity will allow mobile public safety personnel to use software applications to easily exchange media-rich information for emergency response and recovery.

Table 1. Examples of Public Safety Broadband Applications

Video Streaming	A firefighter's helmet camera is streaming real-time video back to an emergency operations center. Video surveillance feed from an ensuing crime scene is sent to dispatch and then to multiple responders within seconds.
Mapping/ Location-Based Services	Geocoded police points of interest appear on a map on an officer's mobile device as they move about a jurisdiction; map push-pins represent addresses flagged for known hazards and include drill-down information such as street level photos and recent crime data.
Large Data File Transfers	Detailed images from a disaster scene are integrated with incident management databases for decision by incident commanders. Building blueprints are sent to a firefighter's hardened mobile device.
Telemetry	Emergency medical personnel place sensors on a patient during an event and transmit vital signs to the nearest hospital. Temperature sensors from firefighter devices generate a heat map of a building interior, allowing civil engineers to determine the structural integrity of the building.

Mobile applications and services are one of the largest, fastest-growing commercial markets in the world. Table 1 provides several examples of public safety broadband applications in use today. Such solutions—developed as part of the broader, commercially-based, broadband communications ecosystem—will constantly evolve and improve along with innovations in commercial technology.

With the adoption of broadband technologies and applications, understanding and preparing for the security risks associated with the open architecture and vast complexity of Internet-based technologies and services will be critical for the public safety community. Cybersecurity, for example, is becoming a key consideration for public safety officials as new Internet Protocol-enabled technology is integrated into their operations. This will require the public safety community to implement effective strategies to enhance the resiliency of cyber and Internet Protocol-based infrastructures and safeguard private or sensitive information transmitted and stored by connected systems and devices.[16,17]

In order to meet these challenges, a multifaceted approach will be needed to ensure the confidentiality, integrity, reliability, and availability of data. For example, comprehensive cyber training and education on the proper use and security of devices and applications, phishing, malware, other potential threats, and how to stay on guard against attacks will be required. In addition, planning must match user needs against bandwidth requirements and the options for network resiliency. Finally, assessments of cyber risks and strategies to mitigate vulnerabilities must be conducted before the deployment of Internet Protocol-based networks occurs to ensure that mission requirements can be met securely and reliably from the outset. For public safety communications, strong security features will need to be built into the design and deployment of the Nationwide Public Safety Broadband Network, with the appropriate layers of control and security at both the core and access networks.

2.3. Modernizing Emergency Communications: Communications and Information Exchange across the Whole Community

In addition to the Nationwide Public Safety Broadband Network, communication network modernization is occurring in other parts of emergency management and response communities, with significant ramifications for communications and coordination in the field. Among these developments are efforts to update the Nation's 9-1-1 infrastructure to Next Generation 9-1-1, an Internet Protocol-based model that will enable the transmission of digital information (e.g., texts, images, and video). In addition, the deployment of a nationwide public alerting system is using traditional media, such as broadcast and cable, as well as Internet Protocol-based technologies to transmit alerts to mobile phones and other devices.

While communications among responders play the most direct and immediate role in saving lives and protecting property, responders can be supported by communications from other stakeholders working collectively in the greater environment. As a result, a broader emergency communications ecosystem has emerged that consists of many inter-related components and functions, including communications for incident response operations, notifications and alerts and warnings, requests for assistance and reporting, and public information exchange.[18] The primary functions are depicted in Exhibit 2 and described below.

- **Communications for Incident Response and Coordination.** These are primarily government-to-government functions that encompass communications between responders in the field, communications between a dispatch center and responders, and communications between government agencies at various levels providing incident support. These types of communications are critical for establishing command and control, conducting operations, and maintaining situational awareness during incidents. The primary communications networks that serve this function include Land Mobile Radio, commercial and private wired and wireless broadband networks, and, once it becomes fully operational, the Nationwide Public Safety Broadband Network.

- **Notifications and Alerts and Warnings.** This key communications function involves issuing alerts, warnings, and incident-related information, primarily from government agencies over privately owned communications networks and services to individuals, private sector entities, and nongovernmental organizations. The primary objective of alerts and warnings is to communicate potential threat and safety-related information to advise and protect the public in emergency situations. Prior to anticipated incidents (e.g., hurricanes, severe storms, or floods), the government may issue alerts and warnings such as evacuation notices or other information to help the public prepare. Following an incident, messaging from government agencies and public information officers is vital to relaying time-sensitive information on immediate response and recovery-related services to the general public. Several key communications systems enable this function, including the Integrated Public Alert and Warning System—which consists of the Emergency Alert System and Wireless Emergency Alert system—the National Warning System, and the National Oceanic and Atmospheric Administration Weather Radio All Hazards. DHS' National Cybersecurity and Communications Integration Center and the National Infrastructure Coordinating Center also provide incident-related information to critical infrastructure owners and operators so they can take necessary action. In addition to these systems, more government agencies are using social media to relay time-sensitive warnings and information to the public.

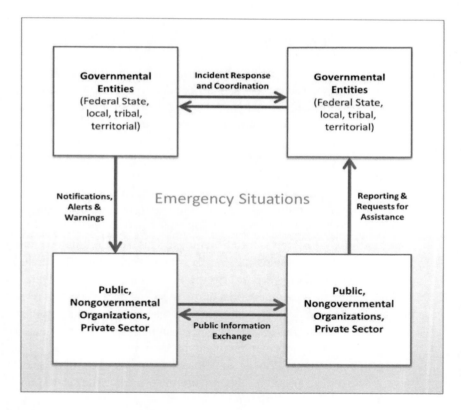

Exhibit 2. Emergency Communications Ecosystem.

- **Public Information Exchange.** Individuals often provide situational awareness to their family members and communities during incidents. This function is primarily supported by commercial networks, including the increasing use of social media by individuals and entities during emergencies. This function also applies to communications and information sharing from and between private sector entities that support government response, including utility companies and critical infrastructure operators that share information on the availability of their services, resources, and status of service restoration.
- **Requests for Assistance and Reporting.** Emergencies are often first reported to authorities by members of the public seeking assistance. Emergency 9-1-1 systems are the key communications systems that support this function. In the future, Next Generation 9-1-1 will enhance the capabilities of current 9-1-1 networks, allowing the public to transmit pictures, videos, and text messages that will provide additional situational awareness to dispatchers and emergency responders. In addition to calls to Public Safety Answering Points and Public Safety Communications Centers, programs such as the DHS "See Something, Say Something" campaign have increased the number of reports and tips from concerned individuals to government agencies, as has the use of social media. In addition, amateur radio operators also serve as key contributors in this function as they can be important conduits for relaying information to response agencies and personnel when other forms of communications have failed or have been disrupted. Some nongovernmental and private sector entities support this function by providing situational awareness of an incident to assist the government with response and recovery (e.g., utilities reporting on the status of service outages, commercial communications companies reporting infrastructure and service outages to the Federal Communications Commission (FCC) through the Disaster Information Reporting System and the Network Outage Reporting System.[19,20]

Modernization of these emergency communications components is facilitating the flow of information and communications among government agencies, the private sector, and the public, and in some cases, with entities from neighboring countries. The sample scenario in Exhibit 3 demonstrates the potential benefits of these interconnected emergency communications functions, including enhanced situational awareness, operational coordination, and decision-making.[21] Wireless broadband networks and applications will greatly influence incident operations as they become more prevalent and are more widely adopted by emergency responders. As a result, the scenario provided in Exhibit 3 will likely begin to occur more frequently.

Following a collision with a telephone pole, the driver of an overturned oil tanker truck texts a 9-1-1 operator that he is trapped in his vehicle's cabin. The 9-1-1 operator provides the information to several responders identified as being closest to the incident by their geo-location, including a police officer, a firefighter, two Emergency Medical Services units, and a hazardous materials team. A woman at the scene simultaneously uses social media capabilities on her smartphone to send photos to authorities and raise awareness among neighbors.

Having already been alerted to the unusual traffic congestion caused by the accident through a traffic-monitoring application, the police officer is already on the way using the quickest path, thanks to a dynamic routing application provided via smartphone and synched with the vehicle's audio system and video display.

Meanwhile, the electric utility company has been alerted to damage its infrastructure sustained during the incident through its continuous monitoring system. A repair team is dispatched to ensure power at the site and in the vicinity.

Based on photos and video provided by the public that identify the truck and its crash disposition, the Public Safety Answering Point is able to share information from the ground quickly so that responders can make quick and accurate decisions regarding the likely risk associated with the oil tanker crash and the mitigation steps responders should take.

The Public Safety Answering Point remotely selects the responding personnel through a public safety application loaded on their Internet Protocol-enabled mobile devices. Each responder is displayed on a local map with his/her skillset profile and an estimated time of arrival on scene. It also displays any resources that may be of use, such as fire hydrants and medical facilities. With this knowledge in hand, responders use their interoperable Project 25 radios to initiate voice communications and coordinate with each other in advance of arrival.

Video of the incident is now streaming to each first responder's smartphone from a traffic camera adjusted to give the best view of the incident. The traffic signs at local highways have all automatically adjusted to route traffic around the incident using machine-to-machine communications.

Public alerting authorities and local news stations have placed indications of the accident on Twitter and Facebook. Government alerts have been texted to smartphones in the incident area. Alerting mapping applications allows the public to avoid the accident route.

The 9-1-1 operator has been able to text the truck driver with an estimated response time. In addition, the operator has provided health information provided by the truck driver directly to Emergency Medical Services responders. When the emergency medical personnel make contact, they outfit the driver with sensors and upload his vital signs to the nearest hospital.

Enabled by broadband, responders arrive on scene with: (1) the full medical profile of the trapped driver; (2) foreknowledge of the priority actions to take to mitigate risks associated with the damaged oil tanker; (3) awareness of the arrival times and skill sets of other responders; (4) integrated support from the power utility and a hospital; and (5) the ability to focus on the incident, rather than a need for significant traffic management. In addition, communications applications and responder-enabled video gear has archived the incident response for precise after action reporting.

Exhibit 3. Emergency Communications Ecosystem at Work- A Potential Scenario.

In addition to the benefits of this increased flow of communications and information, there are potential communications challenges for the emergency response community. While improvements in the quantity, quality, occurrence, timeliness, and type of information available to responders can enhance information sharing and communications during operations, they can also overload or degrade the information if the flow is not interoperable, properly secured, and managed so that the right information gets to the right people, at the right time. This reinforces the need for joint decision- making, planning, and investments to coordinate mutually-supportive strategies as Next Generation 9-1-1, the Nationwide Public Safety Broadband Network, nationwide public alerting systems, and other major capabilities are deployed across the Nation.

"Future 911 systems will use Internet protocols to facilitate interoperability and system resilience, and to provide better connections between 911 call centers, emergency responders, and alert and warning systems ... Operational convergence of emergency communications seems to many to be inevitable, a question of "when," not "if." There is a growing realization among public safety officials, policy makers and others that 911 services could be part of a larger solution for emergency communications that links citizens with first responders and with emergency services such as hospitals through an interconnected system of communications networks and call centers."

   – **Congressional Research Service** "An Emergency Communications Safety Net: Integrating 911 and Other Services"

3.0. NATIONAL EMERGENCY COMMUNICATIONS PLAN STRATEGIC COMPONENTS

The National Emergency Communications Plan provides strategic direction and recommended key next steps for the emergency response community in an evolving communications landscape. For example, governance structures and processes need to address both current mission critical and emerging technologies; strategic plans must account for the sustainment of Land Mobile Radio and the continued integration of broadband; and training and exercises will need to emphasize lessons learned and prepare for entirely new operational processes. These priorities need to evolve to address the modernization of emergency communications, as well as the role of the whole community supporting incident communications.[22]

As depicted in Exhibit 1, the National Emergency Communications Plan strategy reflects a focus on the people, processes, and technology that are critical components to ensuring successful emergency communications under all threats and hazards. The National Emergency Communications Plan is structured around five strategic **goals** that drive the emergency response community toward the Plan's vision. Each goal is supported by a series of **objectives**; within each objective there are several actionable **recommendations** for various partners. They also promote the goals of the *Homeland Security Act of 2002*, such as the need to identify interoperability and continuity capabilities; identify obstacles to deploying interoperable capabilities; and recommend short- and long-term measures to enhance coordination and communication among Federal, State, local, tribal, and territorial governments.[23] As with the 2008 National Emergency Communications Plan, the Office of Emergency Communications will work with its partners to develop appropriate strategies and benchmarks to accomplish the recommendations.

The National Emergency Communications Plan's objectives and recommendations promote the concepts outlined in Presidential Policy Directive – 8: *National Preparedness*; the *National Preparedness Goal*; the *National Incident Management System*; and the *National Planning Frameworks*. While the majority of the proposed recommendations in the National Emergency Communications Plan support the Response mission area and the Operational Communications core capability identified in the *National Preparedness Goal*, many of the actions also foster integration and inter-relationships among all five mission areas—Prevention, Protection, Mitigation, Response, and Recovery.

Emergency Communications during the Boston Marathon Bombings – April 2013

"Interoperability was a success story. Over the years, millions of dollars have been invested under local, regional and state interoperability plans, and our investments in mutual aid channels, tactical channel plans, radio towers, new radios, and specialized training allowed first responders, as well as command level personnel, to effectively communicate by radio between agencies, between disciplines, and between jurisdictions."

– **Kurt N. Schwartz**, Undersecretary for Homeland Security & Homeland Security Advisor Director,
Massachusetts Emergency Management Agency
Testimony before the House Homeland Security Committee

3.1. Goal 1: Governance and Leadership

Enhance decision-making, coordination, and planning for emergency communications through strong governance structures and leadership

Role of Governance and Leadership in Emergency Communications

When the 2008 National Emergency Communications Plan was released, the Nation was confronting a number of long-standing mission critical voice communications issues—notably, operability, interoperability, and continuity challenges among emergency responders. These challenges were compounded by the lack of coordination among emergency communications disciplines and jurisdictions, often leading to disjointed approaches to planning and the acquisition of disparate radio systems that were not interoperable with neighboring localities.

> **2012 National Emergency Communications Plan Progress Report Key Governance Findings**
>
> The percentage of jurisdictions with governance capabilities at the most advanced level – formal decision-making groups that are involved in strategic planning for emergency communications – was double that of the SAFECOM Baseline Survey in 2006.

The National Emergency Communications Plan was a key step toward increasing coordination across the emergency response community by promoting governance as a top national priority. DHS components helped implement this Plan by targeting grant policies, technical assistance offerings, and other activities to support coordination, planning, and decision-making across all levels of government, jurisdictions, and disciplines. Moving forward, DHS will continue to work with its stakeholders to build and update robust governance structures. These structures are important to maintaining current voice systems and ensuring that the planning, investment, and deployment of broadband systems incorporate emergency responders' needs and requirements.

Advancements in Governance and Leadership

To drive progress in this area, DHS has worked closely with its stakeholders to establish formal governance structures and processes at all levels of government—both domestically and internationally—and to improve coordination between the emergency response community and the private sector. Recognizing the need for statewide coordination, the Office of Emergency Communications partnered with State and territorial officials to support the creation and ongoing operation of Statewide Interoperability Governing Bodies or Statewide Interoperability Executive Committees in every State and territory. Statewide Interoperability Governing Bodies and Statewide Interoperability Executive Committees serve as the primary steering groups for statewide interoperability activities.

The Office of Emergency Communications also provided guidance and support to increase the number of Statewide Interoperability Coordinators and created the National Council of Statewide Interoperability Coordinators to foster information sharing and coordination among emergency communications leaders. Statewide Interoperability Coordinators serve as the central coordination point for the daily operations of a State's interoperability efforts. They are critical for implementing the Statewide Communication Interoperability Plan and coordinating governance activities, grants, training and exercises, and policy development to enhance interoperability throughout their State or territory.[24]

At the Federal-level, coordination on interoperability issues was limited prior to the release of the 2008 National Emergency Communications Plan. The Emergency Communications Preparedness Center, comprised of 14 Federal departments and agencies, was in the early stages of organizing itself as the focal point for coordinating Federal emergency communications activities, including coordinating Federal input to the National Emergency Communications Plan.[25] In 2010, the Emergency Communications Preparedness Center issued its first strategic agenda and has since instituted a collaborative framework that drives coordination on Federal priorities and investments in several key areas, including Federal broadband programs and emergency communications grants. In addition, DHS established the One DHS Emergency Communications Committee to coordinate intra- DHS emergency communications activities.

Enhancements in governance also extend to State and territorial collaboration within and between regions and with international partners. For example, in 2009, the Federal Emergency Management Agency (FEMA) appointed Disaster Emergency Communications Regional Emergency Communications Coordinators to support the administration of the Regional Emergency Communications Coordination Working Groups in each of the 10 FEMA Regions. These and other regional activities, including the Office of Emergency Communications' Regional Coordination Program, have helped form relationships between States and territories on key emergency communications planning and response actions.

In addition, coordination with international partners has expanded through the establishment of partnerships such as the Southwest Border Communications Working Group and the Canada – United States Communications Interoperability Working Group. Both working groups provide opportunities to align interoperability strategies and to resolve bilateral issues of common interest concerning cross- border communications and information exchange.

Key Gaps and Challenges Driving Action

While the growth in governance bodies at the Federal, State, local, tribal, territorial, and regional levels is a significant accomplishment, many of these entities were originally established to address Land Mobile Radio interoperability issues. The emergency response community must now evolve its governing structures to address changes in the environment. Fortunately, there is already a strong foundation for future progress. Federal, State, local, tribal, and territorial governments should focus on expanding or updating current structures, processes, and investments in governance.

A key challenge moving forward will be ensuring coordination between traditional Land Mobile Radio governance programs and other decision-making offices, bodies, and individuals that oversee broadband and technology deployments in States, localities, tribes, and territories. This includes coordination between Statewide Interoperability Coordinators and the State Single Point of Contact for the First Responder Network Authority, if different, as well as with those offices and individuals that oversee technology procurement, information security, budgeting for broadband systems, and emergency management.[26] Collaboration among these individuals, as well as their participation in State governing processes, will ensure coordination between legacy communications planning and maintenance, such as Land Mobile Radio systems and legacy 9-1-1 systems, and the deployment of new technologies and networks, including Next Generation 9-1-1, alerting, and the Nationwide Public Safety Broadband Network.

Further, the dynamic nature of the emergency communications landscape requires frequent assessment of memberships, policies, and priorities of Federal and regional governing bodies to ensure they are positioned to address new challenges. The planning and deployment of the Nationwide Public Safety Broadband Network will also require continued collaboration between the communications and information technology sectors and all levels of government. Increasing these partnerships has many benefits in an evolving operating environment, including the ability to share information and resources, realize potential cost savings, and help responders overcome challenges associated with access and coordination to needed infrastructure and data.

Objectives and Recommendations

The National Emergency Communications Plan strives to ensure that existing governance structures and processes are updated accordingly to foster collaboration on Land Mobile Radio and emerging technologies. The following recommendations are focused on improving cooperation at all levels of government, as well as more effectively coordinating Federal activities and financial assistance programs.

OBJECTIVE 1.1: Strengthen governance structures and processes to enhance State, local, tribal, and territorial collaboration and decision-making. The emergency response community has come together to form a number of successful governance and leadership structures throughout States, localities, tribes, and territories across the Nation, including the establishment of Statewide Interoperability Coordinators, Statewide Interoperability Governing Bodies, and Statewide Interoperability Executive Committees. They were initially focused on Land Mobile Radio issues; however, with the emergence of new technologies and users, these governing bodies must expand their focus to address new technologies and other developments.

Recommendations:

- Update governance structures and processes to address the evolving operating environment. With assistance from DHS, State, local, tribal, and territorial jurisdictions should assess their existing governance structures to ensure they are positioned to address current and emerging policy, technology, and planning developments. This could include adding representatives to Statewide Interoperability Governing Bodies and Statewide Interoperability Executive Committees from associations, organizations, or agencies that support or rely on communications during response and recovery operations (e.g., emergency management agencies, 9-1-1 boards, hospital associations, utilities, and amateur radio organizations). Border States should also assess the need for international representation. As part of this effort, States, territories, tribes, and jurisdictions should also review and update, as necessary, key operating documents for their Statewide Interoperability Governing Bodies and Statewide Interoperability Executive Committees (e.g., charters, agreements, policies, and procedures) to ensure they are positioned to address new technology deployments and facilitate coordination with the Statewide Interoperability Coordinators. The National Council of Statewide Interoperability Coordinators is positioned to provide additional guidance and coordination for this recommendation.

- **Increase intra-State collaboration of communications, broadband, and information technology activities.** States and territories should develop strategies, processes, and best practices to increase intra-State coordination among leadership offices that oversee emergency communications, information technology, cybersecurity, and broadband programs. For each State or territory, this includes ensuring collaboration among the Statewide Interoperability Coordinators; State Single Point of Contact; chief information officer or chief technology officer; chief information security officer; the director of the State Administrative Agency; and the State's Governor's office, as appropriate. This also applies to coordination between governance structures with communications oversight, such as Statewide Interoperability Governing Bodies, Statewide Interoperability Executive Committees, and 9-1-1 Boards.

Multi-State Collaboration Promotes Understanding of Requirements and Resources

The eight States in FEMA Region IV, along with Arkansas and Louisiana, coordinated to develop a Strategic Interstate Communications Resource Allocation Plan that identifies available communications resources in each of the 10 States that could potentially be deployed to assist another State during a large-scale incident.

- **Increase regional structures or processes to foster multi-State coordination and information sharing.** There has been an increased emphasis on regional coordination to enhance preparedness for incidents that exceed traditional jurisdictional boundaries, such as cyber attacks and large-scale natural disasters, like Hurricane Sandy in 2012. This focus has led to the establishment of more regional organizations across the Nation, such as Regional Emergency Communications Coordination Working Groups and Regional Interoperability Councils that foster multi-State communications coordination, as well as groups like the All Hazards Consortium that focus on general emergency management activities.[27] State, local, tribal, and territorial jurisdictions are encouraged to increase their involvement in these multi-State partnerships through formal agreements, activities, or sharing best practices with neighboring States. They should also look to address activities that cross more than one FEMA Region or involve neighboring countries.

OBJECTIVE 1.2: Leverage the Emergency Communications Preparedness Center to increase coordination of Federal programs and requirements. At the time of the 2008 National Emergency Communications Plan, the Emergency Communications Preparedness Center was a nascent organization focused on building its membership and identifying joint priorities. The Emergency Communications Preparedness Center has since evolved to focus on aligning Federal emergency communications planning and investments, and facilitating resource sharing. As emergency communications technologies and practices evolve, the Emergency Communications Preparedness Center should continue to serve as the focal point on key Federal issues, including outreach and broadband user requirements.

Recommendations:

- **Enable the Emergency Communications Preparedness Center to serve as the Federal focal point for coordination with the First Responder Network Authority.** As an interagency program comprised of 14 Federal departments and agencies with emergency communications responsibilities, the Emergency Communications Preparedness Center is well-positioned to provide the First Responder Network Authority with valuable information on the needs of Federal stakeholders. The Emergency Communications Preparedness Center member agencies represent much of the Federal Government's role in emergency communications, including operational usage, policy, grants, research and development, and technical assistance. To provide efficiency and organizational clarity, the Emergency Communications Preparedness Center will serve as the primary body for Federal coordination with the First Responder Network Authority, including Federal broadband user requirements.[28] Moving forward, the Emergency Communications Preparedness Center should work with the First Responder Network Authority to incorporate Federal requirements; provide an inventory of Federal assets for the Nationwide Public Safety Broadband Network; coordinate Federal research and development activities; and further define the Nationwide Public Safety Broadband Network's potential Federal user base.

- **Increase coordination of public safety and national security and emergency preparedness communications requirements and policies.** national security and emergency preparedness communications refers to the ability of federal departments and their leadership to maintain communications at all times under all circumstances.[29] National security and emergency preparedness and public safety communications capabilities may be linked during responses to large-scale disasters that require Federal, State, local, tribal, and territorial support. The National Security and Emergency Preparedness Communications Executive Committee was established in 2012 to advise the President on national security and emergency preparedness requirements to enhance the survivability, resilience, and future architecture of national security and emergency preparedness communications. Given DHS' responsibilities for both national security and emergency preparedness and public safety communications, the Department should work with its Federal partners to increase coordination and information sharing between the Emergency Communications Preparedness Center and the Executive Committee. Collaboration between these groups can better align Federal communications priorities, requirements, and policies.

- **Promote opportunities to share Federal emergency communications infrastructure and resources.** Given fiscal constraints and the continued need to maintain and upgrade legacy communications systems, Federal agencies should promote infrastructure and resource collaboration across all levels of government. The Emergency Communications Preparedness Center should facilitate the exchange of information on existing Federal systems, planned modernization, or consolidation efforts to help identify opportunities to share infrastructure with Federal, State, local, tribal, and territorial governments. This includes identifying and streamlining processes for shared infrastructure for Land Mobile Radio and other communications systems that support response and recovery operations.

OBJECTIVE 1.3: Enhance the coordination and effectiveness of Federal emergency communications grants and investments. Federal grant programs have played a vital role in building emergency communications capabilities nationwide, particularly related to governance. The Office of Emergency Communications coordinates with the SAFECOM Executive Committee/Emergency Response Council to annually develop the *SAFECOM Guidance on Emergency Communications Grants* to provide recommendations to grantees for improving interoperability.[30] This guidance document is also critical for ensuring consistency across the Federal Government's grant programs for emergency communications. Further, in 2008, the Emergency Communications Preparedness Center established a Grants Focus Group to improve coordination of Federal emergency communications financial assistance programs, including grants, loans, and cooperative agreements. Through the Emergency Communications Preparedness Center Grants Focus Group, Federal agencies with emergency communications grant programs should focus on improving: (1) the coordination of grant policies, priorities, and processes to enhance consistency; and (2) the assessment of grant-funded activities.

> **SAFECOM Guidance on Emergency Communications Grants — Priorities**
>
> • Leadership and Governance
> • Statewide Planning
> • Training and Exercises
> • Activities that Enhance Operational Coordination
> • Standards-Based Equipment

Recommendations:

- **Promote consistent policies across Federal grant programs and investments.** To ensure Federally-funded investments are coordinated, compatible, and interoperable, Federal departments and agencies should adopt and reference common grant guidance, such as the *SAFECOM Guidance on Emergency Communications Grants,* in emergency communications grant program materials. This document provides information to grantees seeking to implement emergency communications projects. It includes recommendations on how to coordinate with statewide leaders to ensure investments align with statewide plans and are not duplicative. Also included are recommendations on procurement of standards-based equipment to ensure Federally-funded investments are compatible and interoperable. To promote consistent policies from the Federal level, DHS will identify effective approaches to procuring emergency communications equipment across multiple technologies. In addition, DHS will provide sample language that State and local entities can use in contract vehicles to support inter- governmental purchasing, reduce duplication in purchases, achieve cost savings, and ensure compliance with technical standards that promote interoperability. At the same time, the Emergency Communications Preparedness Center Grants Focus Group should continue to drive the development and adoption of common policies, procedures, terminology, and grant guidance for Federal departments and agencies. This includes increasing the use of the *Emergency Communications Preparedness Center Recommendations to Federal Agencies: Financial Assistance for Emergency Communications* and the *Emergency Communications Preparedness Center Federal Financial Assistance Reference Guide,* which aim to improve Federal agencies' understanding of key policies and technological standards that promote interoperability.[31]

- **Improve the ability to assess the impact of emergency communications grant funding.** The Emergency Communications Preparedness Center Grants Focus Group should coordinate efforts to enhance the Federal Government's ability to understand, assess, and report on Federal funding for emergency communications activities. Central to this effort is implementing a standard approach for collecting emergency communications data at the project level. The success of this initiative will require participation from all Federal departments and agencies responsible for administering emergency communications grants.

3.2. Goal 2: Planning and Procedures

Update plans and procedures to improve emergency responder communications and readiness in a dynamic operating environment

Role of Planning and Procedures in Emergency Communications

Strong governance and partnerships can facilitate another key component of successful emergency communications—the development of strategies, plans, and operating procedures. Plans and operating procedures are especially critical in the current operating environment, as they can help Federal, State, local, tribal, and territorial governments manage their future mission critical voice needs and capabilities, as well as the deployment of new mobile data services and applications. To meet this challenge, response agencies at all levels of government will need to assess their strategic, business, operational, and tactical planning needs on a regular basis and update them as needed.

Advancements in Planning and Procedures

The 2008 National Emergency Communications Plan established a planning framework to guide diverse stakeholder efforts at all levels of government. As a result, all 56 States and territories have formal planning processes, led by their Statewide Interoperability Coordinators, to develop, implement, and update statewide strategic plans. The Statewide Communication Interoperability Plans have been useful in bringing together the emergency communications stakeholder community to identify near- and long-term initiatives to improve communications.

> **Standard Operating Procedure Progress — National Emergency Communications Plan Goals Findings**
>
> • Significant increase of jurisdictions having developed formal Standard Operating Procedures compared to 2006 SAFECOM Baseline Survey;
> • More jurisdictions reported using Standard Operating Procedures during response operations;
> • Increase in the adoption of National Incident Management System in Standard Operating Procedures, including greater use of plain language and Incident Command System forms for communications, such as Incident Radio Communications Plans (Incident Command System Form 205).

At the local level, DHS has coordinated the development of Tactical Interoperable Communications Plans in more than 150 jurisdictions. The Department has also worked with many States and all 10 FEMA Regions to develop Regional Emergency Communications Plans.

In addition, there has been an increase in both the development and use of emergency communications standard operating procedures nationwide. Public safety organizations' focus on these procedures has helped establish a more consistent and comprehensive approach for establishing intra- and interagency communications following an incident, enabling effective emergency responses to disasters and incidents such as Hurricane Sandy and the Boston Marathon bombings.

Key Gaps and Challenges Driving Action

To date, most emergency communications plans and procedures have focused on achieving operability and interoperability of mission critical voice communications capabilities. Given the rapidly evolving operating environment, agencies and jurisdictions will need to update or develop new strategies to guide the investment, deployment, and security of both Land Mobile Radio and broadband communications systems. This includes planning and procedures for how spectrum will be used during emergencies, such as which entities are authorized to transmit on specific frequencies and what they are allowed to broadcast. Furthermore, given that responsibilities for emergency communications and information technology are many times led by different agencies, coordination is critical to ensure consistent priorities and strategies for deploying broadband services across States and territories. As an example, since some emergencies may require unplanned spectrum assignment changes, agency spectrum managers should be involved in emergency communications planning and operations.

In addition, as the emergency response community continues to integrate broadband services and technologies into their daily operations, DHS will work with public and private sector entities to refine their existing tactical plans, policies, and standard operating procedures. The DHS Critical Infrastructure Partnership Advisory Council is a mature partnership to leverage for coordinating planning across sectors that are involved in emergency communications, including the communications, information technology, intergovernmental, and emergency services sectors.[32]

Objectives and Recommendations

The following objectives and recommendations provide guidance to agencies at all levels of government to position their strategic, operational, and business planning initiatives in the evolving emergency communications environment.

OBJECTIVE 2.1: Increase strategic planning at all levels of government to address emergency communication gaps, new technologies, and stakeholders. Federal, State, local, tribal, and territorial emergency response agencies should update existing or develop new strategic plans to address current emergency communications capabilities and gaps, as well as the deployment and use of new technologies (e.g., broadband, Next Generation 9-1-1, common alerting protocols, and social media).[33] In addition, to facilitate coordination and information exchange throughout the broader community, strategic planning for emergency communications should incorporate entities from across the Information Sharing Environment, as appropriate.[34] The Federal Government will continue to coordinate and support national strategic planning efforts for emergency communications through guidance and provision of support services, such as technical assistance and grant guidance.

Recommendations:

- **Update Statewide Communication Interoperability Plans to maintain Land Mobile Radio systems and address wireless**

broadband deployments. States and territories should update their Statewide Communication Interoperability Plans to plan for the deployment of wireless broadband services, while maintaining and enhancing legacy emergency communications systems and functions (e.g., Land Mobile Radio, Public Safety Answering Points, and Public Safety Communications Centers). In addition, Statewide Interoperability Coordinators are encouraged to collaborate with other communications and technology officials within their State/territory (e.g., State chief information officers, chief technology officers, and chief information security officers) to ensure a consistent approach on statewide planning activities for new technology deployments. As part of this effort, States should consider involving neighboring States in the development of the Statewide Communication Interoperability Plan. States and territories should continue to report progress in implementing their Statewide Communication Interoperability Plans to the Office of Emergency Communications on an annual basis.

Statewide Communication Interoperability Plan Workshops Promote Interoperability, Enhanced 9-1-1 Efforts

In 2013, the State of Iowa held its first joint planning workshop between the Statewide Interoperable Communications Systems Board and the Enhanced 9-1-1 Communications Council. As a result of this workshop, participants developed joint and separate goals and initiatives that were eventually incorporated into Iowa's Statewide Communications Interoperability Plan to support the strategic joint vision and mission of the Enhanced 9-1-1 Council and Iowa Statewide Interoperable Communications Systems Board. The two governing bodies have continued to collaborate on the implementation of the plan and other initiatives.

- **Coordinate Federal strategic planning for broadband capabilities through the Emergency Communications Preparedness Center.** Decision-makers within Federal departments and agencies should determine how their organizations could benefit from broadband technology to either improve or augment legacy capabilities. To inform Federal broadband planning efforts, Federal departments and agencies should coordinate their broadband requirements (e.g., coverage, roaming, priority access, and user base), as well as potential costs and applications, through the Emergency Communications Preparedness Center Broadband Focus Group. In turn, the Emergency Communications Preparedness Center will coordinate Federal input to the First Responder Network Authority for Nationwide Public Safety Broadband Network planning and development activities.

- **Enable One DHS to lead the implementation of a DHS strategic plan for emergency communications.** The One DHS Emergency Communications Committee will coordinate the implementation and track progress of a Department-wide integrated communications interoperability plan. The DHS plan will establish goals and priorities to improve interoperable and emergency communications, including Land Mobile Radio voice integration with broadband data technology. It will also provide a shared understanding of the roles, responsibilities, and ongoing initiatives for integrating parallel emergency communications activities across the Department.

OBJECTIVE 2.2: Increase preparation for the adoption and deployment of the Nationwide Public Safety Broadband Network and wireless broadband technologies at all levels of government. Federal, State, local, tribal, and territorial entities should conduct comprehensive outreach and planning to ensure that the deployment of broadband systems and technologies, including the Nationwide Public Safety Broadband Network, meets their responders' communications needs at initial operating capability and beyond. This includes having a complete understanding of their current broadband usage and coverage requirements. It also requires coordination with the First Responder Network Authority, as the final authority on Nationwide Public Safety Broadband Network-related decisions, to ensure input to and implementation of the business plan for building the foundational elements of the organization and the Nationwide Public Safety Broadband Network infrastructure. As an example, the National Public Safety Telecommunications Council has developed a series of user requirements to assist the First

Responder Network Authority in the Nationwide Public Safety Broadband Network's design and architecture.[35]

> **State Broadband Planning**
>
> "The decision of a state to accept, or "opt-in," to the First Responder Network Authority's proposed plan for that state, or to not accept, and "opt-out" of that plan will be a major one. It is the goal of the First Responder Network Authority to develop an environment of "opt-in" throughout the country."
>
> – **Samuel Ginn**
> Former Chairman, First Responder Network Authority Board
> Testimony Before the House Subcommittee on Communications and Technology

Recommendations:

- **Ensure Nationwide Public Safety Broadband Network planning is coordinated throughout each State and territory and focuses on responders' current and future needs.** The Single Point of Contact within each State and territory should coordinate with local jurisdictions and tribal nations to document their current broadband usage, identify user needs, and establish baseline Nationwide Public Safety Broadband Network coverage requirements. States and territories should also identify potential infrastructure that can be shared to fill gaps in network deployment to ensure reduced network costs and economies of scale.[36,37] State and territorial Single Point of Contact should also coordinate with local jurisdictions to develop a methodology to prioritize future broadband coverage needs.
- **Establish points of contact to coordinate Federal broadband planning and deployment activities.** Federal departments and agencies are encouraged to identify points of contact—whether an individual, office, or process—to coordinate key planning activities related to the Nationwide Public Safety Broadband Network's deployment.[38] These points of contact should collaborate with the Emergency Communications Preparedness Center, which will coordinate overall Federal broadband activities for the First Responder Network Authority, including Federal coverage requirements and infrastructure sharing.

- **Expand lifecycle planning activities to address broadband deployments and security, as needed.** Public safety agencies at all levels of government are encouraged to expand their system lifecycle planning efforts for current mission critical Land Mobile Radio systems to address the deployment of any planned broadband systems and other technologies, such as information technology services. Broadening lifecycle planning can improve coordination and planning of system refresh and replacement activities in support of the long-term transition to broadband systems. In addition, given the increased cybersecurity threats that could compromise broadband systems, agencies' lifecycle planning should analyze, address, and monitor system risks.

OBJECTIVE 2.3: Improve emergency responders' ability to communicate and share information through comprehensive standard operating procedures. As more emergency responders adopt new technologies and applications, standard operating procedures will be critical for responders to coordinate and use communications equipment and facilities during response and recovery operations. In some cases, procedures may need to be updated to address entities, individuals, or organizations that provide or use communications during emergencies (e.g., utilities, the transportation sector, commercial carriers). In support of this recommendation, DHS will periodically update and publish the National Interoperability Field Operations Guide to ensure that it provides up-to- date radio frequency information to assist those establishing or repairing emergency communications in a disaster area.

Recommendations:

- **Evaluate, update, and distribute standard operating procedures to address new technologies and align them to tactical plans.** Jurisdictions and agencies should periodically assess and revise their standard operating procedures to ensure they appropriately incorporate new technologies used during response and recovery operations. This includes accounting for social media as a means of disseminating and receiving information to and from the public. Standard operating procedures should also align with a jurisdiction's existing tactical plans (e.g., Tactical Interoperable Communications Plans) to achieve interoperable emergency communications and be widely distributed to users—including other emergency response entities such as utility companies, public health and medical organizations, or nongovernmental organizations, as appropriate.
- **Ensure standard operating procedures reflect current use of priority telecommunications services.** All levels of government should periodically review the priority service programs (e.g., Telecommunications Service Priority, Government Emergency Telecommunications Service, and Wireless Priority Service) to which they subscribe and ensure they have standard operating procedures governing the programs' use, execution, and testing. Key elements of the standard operating procedures should include the capabilities of each service; the method and points of contact to activate or subscribe to them; guidelines for usage and training; and potential cost recovery mechanisms available for use during State or Federally-declared disasters.[39]
- **Coordinate with entities from across the broader emergency response community to develop communications standard operating procedures.** As agencies review and update their emergency communications standard operating procedures, they are encouraged to involve entities that directly provide, use, or support communications during emergencies. This may include local, tribal, territorial, and regional entities, as well as international partners, auxiliary responders, and industry representatives, as appropriate. Further, standard operating procedures should include contact information for key industry representatives to provide access to timely communications resources and expedite restoration efforts (e.g., infrastructure owners and operators, public health, medical,

public works, transportation entities, utility companies, and commercial telecommunications carriers).

3.3. Goal 3: Training and Exercises

Improve responders' ability to coordinate and communicate through training and exercise programs that use all available technologies and target gaps in emergency communications

Role of Training and Exercises in Emergency Communications

Effective training and exercise programs can bolster emergency responders' proficiency with communications equipment, as well as improve their ability to execute policies, plans, and procedures governing the use of communications. Continuing to train on Land Mobile Radio systems is necessary to ensure that emergency responders can achieve mission critical voice communications. However, as wireless broadband and other communications technologies become integrated into response and recovery operations, the need for training and exercises becomes even more critical to ensure that response personnel are routinely practicing with new communications capabilities to maximize their benefits.

Advancements in Training and Exercises

Improving emergency responders' skills and capabilities was one of the 2008 National Emergency Communications Plan's top priorities. Since then, notable strides have been made toward increasing the availability of emergency communications-specific training courses and field exercises. In recent years, DHS has designed and conducted multiple exercises under the Homeland Security Exercise and Evaluation Program to assess the Nation's response capabilities, including communications interoperability and continuity. Several of these were functional exercises, like the 2011 National Level Exercise, that tested communications among multi- jurisdictional and multi-disciplinary emergency responders, command posts, agencies, and government officials.[40,41]

DHS has worked closely with public safety agencies across the Nation to increase training opportunities for their communications personnel. For example, more than 4,000 emergency responders have taken DHS' All-Hazards Communications Unit Leader course, and more than 1,000 have taken the Department's Communications Technician course.[42] Both of these positions are critical for communications operability and interoperability—especially the functionality of communications equipment during incidents or planned events.

In addition to training, DHS has worked with States, localities, tribes, and territories to develop exercise programs that target their most pressing emergency communications issues. The Office of Emergency Communications Technical Assistance Program has helped State, territories, local jurisdictions, and tribal nations design, execute, and evaluate communications-focused tabletop, full-scale, and functional exercises to address gaps specific to their communications needs. In addition, the Office of Emergency Communications' implementation of the 2008 National Emergency Communications Plan showed that regular training and exercising have a direct correlation to operational effectiveness.[43]

Key Gaps and Challenges Driving Action

While States and territories have made progress to ensure training and exercises support the communications needs of their emergency responders, various challenges still remain. Reductions in budgets that support State, local, tribal, and territorial training and exercise programs have made it difficult for some States to establish formal oversight bodies to recognize and train Communications Unit personnel, which presents challenges with consistency in certification criteria. Further, turnover and reduction of staff have made it critical to efficiently educate new personnel on emergency communications equipment, protocols, and responsibilities. These issues can be compounded by logistical challenges associated with responder participation in formal training and exercise activities, as they may require shifting staff schedules, overtime pay, and increased time commitment, and travel.

The National Emergency Communications Plan recognizes the impact that these challenges can have on the availability and frequency of communications-focused training and exercise programs. At the same time, in order to be effective, these programs will need to evolve to reflect the changing operating environment. This means that agencies must assess their programs to ensure they align with national response doctrine, such as the *National Incident Management System* and the *National Response Framework*; account for new communications technologies being used by responders; and address gaps identified during assessments and after-action reports.

Public safety agencies will also need to broaden the scope of their training and exercise programs to address communications and information sharing with new entities, as well as the use of new technologies. As discussed in Section 2.0, communications from other sources, such as Public Safety Answering Points and Public Safety Communications Centers, the private sector, volunteer organizations, and the general public, are impacting operational coordination and decision-making for public safety officials. Training and exercises will be critical for emergency responders to foster coordination with these partners, as well as to manage and filter the large amounts of information (i.e., data, video, and voice communications) from these sources. Moving forward, public safety agencies will need to consider training and exercises that involve the broader emergency communications community and account for both Land Mobile Radio and broadband, as appropriate.

Objectives and Recommendations

The 2008 National Emergency Communications Plan training and exercise milestones were focused on two key areas: (1) expanding communication-specific exercises around the Nation; and (2) developing standardized training for emergency responders who use or manage communications resources, mainly Land Mobile Radio systems. While this Plan seeks to build on the success of those initiatives, it also emphasizes the need for Federal, State, local, tribal, and territorial entities to regularly assess and update their training curricula and exercise criteria to reflect changes in the operating environment. In addition, this Plan provides suggestions to make the most efficient use of training and exercise opportunities given budget constraints, as well as recommendations to maximize the benefits of using trained Communications Unit personnel during response operations.[44]

OBJECTIVE 3.1: Update training and exercise programs to address gaps in emergency communications, as well as emerging technologies, policies, and partners. As communications technologies continue to evolve, the need for training and exercises becomes even greater to ensure personnel are proficient in the increasing number of diverse capabilities used during incident response. Agencies will need to assess and update their training and exercise programs to ensure relevancy and completeness, and incorporate changes in policies, procedures, partners, and technologies. This includes revising training and exercises to ensure consistency with the Homeland Security Exercise and Evaluation Program and national response doctrine and guidance, such as the *National Incident Management System* and the *National Response Framework.*

Recommendations:

- **Develop training and exercise programs that target gaps in emergency communications capabilities and use of new technologies.** federal, state, local, tribal, and territorial entities should review after-action reports from real-world incidents and exercises to determine how they can incorporate lessons learned into the objectives for their training and exercise programs. This may include addressing resource gaps, lack of adherence to procedures, areas for improvement with Land Mobile Radio, or other challenges. Programs should also reflect the use of new communications technologies, including mobile broadband, social media, and wireless emergency alerts, as appropriate.

- **Identify opportunities to integrate more private and public sector communications stakeholders into training and exercises.** Federal, State, local, tribal, and territorial jurisdictions should identify domestic and international entities with potential roles in information sharing and the delivery of emergency communications during emergencies (e.g., utility companies, amateur radio operators, nongovernmental organizations, media companies, and telecommunications owners, operators, manufacturers, and suppliers). As appropriate, these entities should be incorporated into training and exercise activities on a more regular basis. This includes involving the appropriate stakeholders in curriculum or exercise design and execution, as necessary.

- **Increase responder proficiency with Federal and national interoperability channels through training and exercises.** Federal agencies should work with emergency response personnel to pre-program Federal and national interoperability channels into their radios and conduct regular training on them. These shared channels are common resources that are useful for initial on-the-scene coordination and communications. To that end, Federal departments and agencies should assess their current communications training curriculum and exercise programs to ensure they address the use of interoperability channels in designated public safety spectrum bands and the National Interoperability Field Operations Guide.[45,46]

> **Communications Interoperability Case Study**
>
> "The Department of Homeland Security (DHS) Office of Emergency Communications conducted an exercise during a previous Boston Marathon to test and train for communications interoperability. Based on lessons learned from this DHS assistance and funding for technology, our emergency radio communications system worked without incident[...] In the past, the police, fire and Emergency Medical Services personnel would not have been able to communicate because of our different radio systems."
>
> – **Edward F. Davis III**
> Commissioner, Boston Police Department, before the U.S. Senate Committee on Homeland Security and Government Affairs July 10, 2013

- **OBJECTIVE 3.2: Increase awareness and availability of emergency communications training and exercise opportunities at all levels of government.** Implementation of the National Emergency Communications Plan and analysis of after-action reports from real-world incidents have shown that participating in training and exercises is a key indicator of an entity's or individual's success in the field. Given the importance of testing, agencies should identify cost-effective approaches for emergency responders to access these activities (e.g., distance learning or local training and exercises). Greater awareness of opportunities can be achieved through use of new technologies, as well as increased messaging of training and exercise opportunities through governance bodies. DHS will continue to support State, local, tribal, and territorial training and exercises through the Office of Emergency Communications' Regional Coordination and Technical Assistance Programs and work with the public safety community to ensure these services continue to stay viable and current.

Recommendations:

- **Use regional governance structures to develop and promote training and exercise opportunities.** Regional governing bodies, such as the Regional Emergency Communications Coordination Working Groups and Regional Interagency Steering Committees, should collect and disseminate information on relevant and beneficial training and exercise opportunities to statewide governing bodies, such as the Statewide Interoperability Governing Bodies and Statewide Interoperability Executive Committees. In turn, State and territorial entities should conduct outreach on training and exercises to increase awareness at the local level and with any tribal nations. This can increase preparation and coordination during cross-border or multi-State incidents.
- **Leverage technologies, conferences, and workshops to increase training and exercise opportunities.** Given budget constraints, Federal, State, local, tribal, and territorial governments should take advantage of scheduled stakeholder meetings and workshops as potential opportunities to develop or hold training, tabletop exercises, or operational-based exercises. These meetings could also serve as opportunities to review certain training standards or discuss communications-related exercise objectives or observations from recent exercises. In addition, agencies are encouraged to leverage new technologies to conduct virtual exercises and create opportunities to evaluate operational performance.

OBJECTIVE 3.3: Enhance the awareness, use, and tracking of trained Communications Unit personnel during response operations. The 2008 National Emergency Communications Plan promoted the development and implementation of national training programs and recognition processes for emergency responders who use or manage communications resources. To help achieve these objectives, the Office of Emergency Communications, in conjunction with the FEMA Emergency Management Institute, implemented Communications Unit Leader and Communications Technician courses to ensure that every State and territory has trained personnel capable of deploying and operating advanced equipment during an incident or planned event. Over the past several years, Communications Unit Leaders and Communications Technicians have been successful in maintaining, reestablishing, and coordinating emergency communications functions during major disasters, including Hurricanes Sandy and Irene, wildfires in Arizona and New Mexico, and tornadoes and ice storms in the South and Midwest. The National Emergency Communications Plan seeks to build on this progress by aiming to have all Communications Unit positions (e.g., Communications Unit Leader, Communications Technician, and Radio Operator) more effectively integrated into operations and to improve States' and territories' capability to track and share trained communications personnel.

Recommendations:

- **Promote awareness of and cross-training among Federal, State, local, tribal, and territorial Incident Command System Communications Unit personnel through training and exercises.** State, local, tribal, and territorial governments are encouraged to develop educational materials and training opportunities for dispatchers, incident commanders, and executive-level leaders to improve their understanding of the roles and responsibilities of the Communications Unit. In addition, joint Federal and State Communications Unit Leader refresher training and communications-focused exercise objectives can help build awareness between the Communications Unit personnel and others in the incident command or command staff. DHS will continue to work with its Federal partners to encourage their participation in State exercises to improve their understanding of the Communications Unit's functions.
- **Develop and share best practices on processes to recognize trained Communications Unit personnel.** States and territories are encouraged to review the National Council of Statewide Interoperability Coordinators-endorsed recognition criteria for Communications Unit personnel and work with their neighboring

States and territories most likely to offer assistance during an incident to develop and implement standardized criteria. The National Council of Statewide Interoperability Coordinators should continue to explore ways to promote recognition criteria, best practices, and lessons learned to improve consistency in Communications Unit training across States and territories.

- **Improve States' and territories' ability to track and share trained Communications Unit personnel during response operations.** The Office of Emergency Communications will coordinate with States and territories to develop and maintain a repository of their trained and recognized Communications Unit personnel. States and territories are encouraged to use tools, such as those hosted on the Office of Emergency Communications' Public Safety Technical Assistance Tools website, to store and share information with neighboring States for personnel deployment.[47] Further, incorporating the dispatch and tracking of Incident Command System Communications Unit personnel into dispatch decision-support programs or policies can help increase the use of trained personnel and improve documentation during response. States and territories should collaborate with Public Safety Answering Points and Public Safety Communications Centers to improve awareness and understanding of how this can be accomplished.

3.4. Goal 4: Operational Coordination

Ensure operational effectiveness through the coordination of emergency communications capabilities, resources, and personnel from across the whole community

Role of Operational Coordination in Emergency Communications

While the National Emergency Communications Plan's first three goals focus on building capabilities to achieve operable and interoperable communications, the fourth goal aims to translate those elements into operational success, ensuring that communications planning, processes, partnerships, and resources are effectively coordinated and utilized during response and recovery operations. Although responders require communications to achieve their mission under all circumstances, the need for interoperable and continuous communications capabilities is especially urgent during large-scale disasters and catastrophic situations. Continuity of communications can be achieved through emergency management assistance compacts or the deployment of Federally-owned communications equipment (e.g., Cellular on Wheels/Cellular on Light Trucks, generators) until State and local officials are able to identify additional resources. In addition to facilitating responder-to-responder coordination, these shared communications tools enable responders to request additional support, coordinate mutual aid, and integrate equipment and personnel into operations.

Advancements in Operational Coordination

Public safety agencies at all levels of government have taken steps to improve their ability to communicate as incidents grow and become more complex. This improvement was evident during responses to many large-scale disasters and emergencies in recent years, including the 2010 Deepwater Horizon Oil Spill; the 2011 Joplin, Missouri, and 2013 Moore, Oklahoma, tornadoes; the 2011 East Coast Earthquake; and the 2013 Boston Marathon bombings. During these and other responses, emergency communications services and needs were effectively coordinated and integrated across disciplines, jurisdictions, and levels of government. In addition, responding jurisdictions used the Emergency Management Assistance Compact and cross-border memoranda of understanding to streamline requests for assistance and expedite deployments of communications resources and personnel between States and bordering countries.

> DHS has seen "a tremendous improvement in capabilities at the state and local level...planning, the exercising and, importantly, the technology has allowed us to build more effective interoperable solutions that allow us to rapidly bring not only the responders to the immediate area, but responders from across the state and in some cases across the nation in a rapid manner."
> – **Craig Fugate,**
>   FEMA Administrator

DHS has worked closely with State, local, tribal, territorial, and private sector partners (e.g., communications manufacturers, carriers, and public-private partnerships) to enhance operational communications for planned events (e.g., national political conventions, Super Bowl, State of the Union Address) and following disasters. The FEMA Disaster Emergency Communications Division has partnered with all 56 States and territories to identify emergency communications capabilities and requirements to expedite the delivery of Federal communications resources and support during large-scale incidents. Additionally, through assistance from the Office of Emergency Communications, States continue to inventory their existing emergency communications capabilities using the Communications Asset Survey and Mapping Tool to better understand the availability and location of emergency communications capabilities.

Agencies and jurisdictions have also increased their proficiency with incident response principles under the *National Incident Management System*, which provide standard structures and procedures to improve coordination and communications. This has led to a more consistent execution of Communications Unit roles and responsibilities, as well as the use of Incident Command System forms, such as Incident Radio Communications Plans. Also, the increase in the use of simple, easily understood language has helped reduce the risk of miscommunication during incident responses.

Key Gaps and Challenges Driving Action

Despite these advancements, the changing operating environment is presenting new challenges to responder communications. Operational coordination is often complicated during large, complex incidents where there are various emergency communications personnel, coordinating structures, protocols, and concepts, in addition to commercial telecommunications networks that are congested or inoperable. In situations like these, proper application of the *National Incident Management System* is critical to ensure that all organizations are following appropriate procedures. While the National Emergency Communications Plan Goals Assessment showed that more jurisdictions are using the *National Incident Management System* concepts, it also identified several remaining inconsistencies in their application, which can be problematic as these inconsistencies can hamper communications personnel and assets from being effectively integrated and synchronized into operations at the incident- level. In addition, knowing how and when to request additional communications-specific resources can be difficult, especially at the outset of a disaster.

Further, communications challenges arising from the 2012 Derecho storm that impacted the Midwest and Mid-Atlantic regions of the United States reinforced the need for reliable and resilient emergency communications networks. As the FCC noted in its storm after-action report, a number of preventable system failures caused major disruptions to communications carriers' networks, preventing the public from connecting to 9-1-1 call centers during and shortly after the storm.[48] Given the deployment of Next Generation 9-1-1 and the important role that it will play in improving situational awareness during response operations, continuity of Public Safety Answering Point and Public Safety Communications Center operations are critical for communicating and coordinating with responders in the field.

Objectives and Recommendations

The following objectives and recommendations seek to improve operational effectiveness by promoting the identification and coordination of communications resources; implementing the *National Incident Management System* and *National Response Framework* components that address communications; and ensuring continuity of operations for emergency communications.

- **OBJECTIVE 4.1: Enhance the ability of jurisdictions to coordinate communications resources and services during emergency situations.** As incidents escalate, communications resources must be able to expand rapidly to meet responders' needs. The ability to identify communications resources and follow the procedures to obtain them is critical to quickly deploying them to the locations where they are most needed. This applies to government communications assets, resources, and capabilities provided by the private sector, nongovernmental organizations, and individuals or volunteer groups. Establishing and regularly updating communication asset inventories can help expedite the speed in which emergency communications resources are requested and integrated into operations. Operational mechanisms, such as emergency management assistance compacts, memoranda of agreements, local mutual aid or assistance agreements, and contracts with the private sector, help States and localities coordinate and share resources across domestic and international borders.

Recommendations:

- **Ensure inventories of emergency communications resources are updated and comprehensive.** In order for assets and personnel to be pre-positioned or rapidly deployed to support an incident, public safety agencies should have a complete understanding of the available communications resources (e.g., radio caches, personnel, supplies, and systems) within their States and neighboring jurisdictions. Public safety agencies, response entities, and communications service providers are encouraged to maintain and share comprehensive inventories of their communications capabilities and assets. Governance and advisory bodies (e.g., Statewide Interoperability Governing Bodies, Regional Emergency Communications Coordination Working Groups) should also coordinate with jurisdictions most likely to request or provide resources to develop and periodically update an inventory of government and private sector communications assets and personnel, including strategic technology reserves. Similarly, Federal departments and agencies should coordinate with DHS to ensure that their communications assets available to support incident response are integrated within Emergency Support Function #2—*Communications*.

> ## Communications Sector Resources
>
> The National Coordinating Center for Telecommunications and the Communications Information Sharing and Analysis Center are valuable resources for sharing information with Federal, State, local, tribal, and territorial jurisdictions on industry-specific communications services, teams, and capabilities that may be leveraged and integrated into response operations. Examples of assets that industry can provide include specialized teams, essential service providers, equipment, and advanced technologies.

- **Enhance jurisdictions' ability to readily request communications resources or assets during operations.** All levels of government should regularly assess and revise any mechanisms and procedures (e.g., memoranda of understanding, memoranda of agreement, and pre-scripted mission assignments) they have in place with other agencies, neighboring States, tribes, local jurisdictions, and private sector entities for coordinating and requesting emergency communications resources, including equipment and personnel. This may include establishing pre-negotiated contracts with private sector entities and nongovernmental organizations for critical resources, such as temporary power. When executing these agreements, jurisdictions should clearly define their requirements so that resource providers can engineer the most efficient and effective solutions.

OBJECTIVE 4.2: Increase the implementation of the National Incident Management System concepts for command, control, and communications. The assessment of the 2008 National Emergency Communications Plan goals showed an increase in the use of the *National Incident Management System* across the Nation, along with enhanced cooperation among law enforcement, fire, emergency medical services, and other disciplines. The results also showed the need to ensure that coordination across these disciplines is fully integrated into pre-planning, and consistently executed in accordance with the *National Response Framework*, the *National Incident Management System*, and Incident Command System command structures and practices. As previously discussed in Goal 3, agencies should continue to train and exercise on key Incident Command System positions, including positions within the Communications Unit, as well as appropriate templates and forms.

Recommendations:

- **Implement Incident Command System communications-related roles, responsibilities, and planning.** Response agencies at all levels of government emphasize the use of standardized *National Incident Management System* practices, plans, and common terminology during incidents involving multiple jurisdictions, disciplines, and agencies to promote unity of effort. As such, all agencies and jurisdictions supporting an incident should be involved in pre-planning, including development of a single incident action plan and a comprehensive Incident Command System Form 205 that identifies interoperability channels for each incident. Further, the Incident Command System also prescribes that the roles of operations section chief and logistics section chief should each be filled by a single individual to reduce possibly duplicative or conflicting orders, improve communications, and enhance information exchange.

- **Ensure operational planning incorporates new technologies and communications partners.** The assessment of the 2008 National Emergency Communications Plan goals found that the majority of responders leverage commercial voice and/or mobile data solutions during incident response. The use of commercial solutions is expected to increase with the deployment of the Nationwide Public Safety Broadband Network, especially for mission critical purposes; however, the role of these technologies is not always fully integrated into communications planning. To prepare for widespread Nationwide Public Safety Broadband Network deployment, DHS should coordinate with appropriate stakeholders to update the Incident Command System Form 205 template to include specific fields for commercial voice and data services.

OBJECTIVE 4.3: Strengthen resilience, security, and continuity of communications throughout response operations. As emergency communications systems and functions become more interconnected, they also become more susceptible to vulnerabilities and disruptions in other parts of the communications ecosystem. Agencies and jurisdictions at all levels of government must plan for the interconnection of voice and data communications throughout the ecosystem. During large-scale events, planning and operations for backup communications need to include all available assets and resources in the impacted incident area. For example, Land Mobile Radio systems may need to be augmented by air and marine mobile communications to create a comprehensive air, sea, and ground network with appropriate levels of security and authentication to ensure continuity of communications. Commercial cellular voice and data networks are often used as backup options as well, but these networks may be overwhelmed by congestion and capacity issues. Achieving secure and resilient voice and data communications across the ecosystem is essential for public safety and emergency management agencies to execute their missions under all circumstances.

Recommendations:

- **Ensure Public Safety Answering Point and Public Safety Communications Center continuity of operations planning**

addresses   systems   and   staffing   to   support   dispatch communications. As part of continuity of operations planning, Public Safety Answering Points and Public Safety Communications Centers should address staffing requirements and technical resources to support their ability to maintain dispatch communications and functions during incidents.[49] This includes succession as well as backup procedures for major systems, such as computer-aided dispatch, radio, and power supply. In addition, Public Safety Answering Point and Public Safety Communications Center continuity of operations planning should incorporate relevant capabilities and assets, such as the Telecommunicator Emergency Response Task Forces initiative.[50] Telecommunicator Emergency Response Task Forces can help States develop programs to train teams that can be quickly mobilized and deployed to assist communications centers in the aftermath of disasters. These efforts can strengthen Public Safety Answering Points' and Public Safety Communications Centers' ability to maintain continuity as the public's main point of contact during crises, while also serving as key coordinators of emergency management activities by dispatching information to responders.

• **Update procedures for implementing backup communications solutions.** In the event that primary network and dispatch services are disrupted following an incident, agencies must be able to quickly implement backup communications solutions. As part of their continuity and backup planning efforts, public safety agencies at all levels of government should establish and update their procedures to determine when and how to request and implement backup systems to avoid single points of failure. Agencies should account for priority service programs (e.g., Telecommunications Service Priority, Wireless Priority Service, and Government Emergency Telecommunications Service) and the use of new technologies in their backup planning and procedures, as well as capabilities that could support coverage and capacity during incidents (e.g., auxiliary communications; satellite communications; batteries and power supplies; air, sea, and ground networks; and specialized support teams). As part of their assessment, agencies should also consider the potential use of communications and information technology sectors' capabilities to support their communications needs.

- **Increase Federal departments' and agencies' preparation and support for local emergency communications needs.** During large-scale incidents, States and localities may require Federal support to provide and maintain operable and interoperable communications in an incident area, as well as support temporary re-establishment of the basic public safety communications infrastructure. To help integrate Federal resources, DHS, as the Federal Emergency Support Function #2 coordinator, should ensure the Emergency Support Function #2 Standard Operating Procedure is regularly updated and comprehensive to ensure primary and support agencies engage in appropriate planning and preparedness activities.

3.5. Goal 5: Research and Development

Coordinate Research, Development, Testing, and Evaluation activities to develop innovative emergency communications capabilities that support the needs of emergency responders

Role of Research, Development, Testing, and Evaluation in Emergency Communications

The growing use of broadband technologies underscores the need for a comprehensive and coordinated research, development, testing, and evaluation strategy to ensure emergency responders have the right communications technologies, tools, and services to accomplish their mission. Research, development, testing, and evaluation programs are critical to identify and develop new commercial products and services that meet the unique needs of public safety officials. Research, development, testing, and evaluation can also help adapt existing commercial-off-the-shelf products for public safety use to realize cost efficiencies, while more quickly delivering innovative commercial solutions to the end-user. The importance of testing and evaluation should not be overlooked, as these processes demonstrate how systems, networks, and equipment can sustain functionality and satisfy user requirements, particularly security, availability, and scalability. As a result, coordinating research, development, testing, and evaluation efforts will help ensure that public safety requirements are fully integrated into new technologies, and that products and services comply with existing standards and can withstand rugged operating environments.

Advancements in Research, Development, Testing, and Evaluation

Recent advancements in public safety communications research and development have focused on developing the next generation of public safety applications and devices. Also, given that Land Mobile Radio will continue to be a critical component of emergency communications, research and development efforts will continue to focus on Project 25 Land Mobile Radio networks, as well as infrastructure that can support Project 25 and long-term evolution networks simultaneously. The DHS Office for Interoperability and Compatibility within the Science and Technology Directorate is the Department's lead for research, development, testing, and evaluation, as well as standards acceleration related to interoperable communications. Successful research and development efforts can be attributed to the impact of research and development efforts involving government, carriers, service providers, vendors, and academia. This includes the Department of Commerce's Public Safety Communications Research Program, which is leading the research, development, testing, and evaluation for public safety long-term evolution networks to support the planning and deployment of the Nationwide Public Safety Broadband Network.[51]

In addition to communications used for government response and recovery, research and development efforts have also improved and modernized communications between the government and the public during emergencies. For example, the Wireless Emergency Alerts system, a component of the Integrated Public Alert and Warning System, provides public safety officials at the Federal, State, local, tribal, and territorial levels with the ability to notify the public of emergency situations in real-time via mobile devices. Led by the DHS Science and Technology Directorate Office for Interoperability and Compatibility, these research, development, testing, and evaluation actions and investments have produced products and tools that have helped public safety officials protect lives and property.

Key Gaps and Challenges Driving Action

The adoption of new technologies for mission critical purposes and emergence of new applications should be integrated into and support existing processes. There are many benefits to using standards- based, open-source, vendor-neutral technologies; however, to meet public safety organizational needs, user requirements must be integrated during the development phase. For instance, the unique propagation characteristics of long-term evolution will bring advanced capabilities to both public safety and the consumer marketplace (e.g., virtual navigation, telemedicine, and crowd casting). To ensure these services can sustain mission critical communications, a number of challenges must be addressed, including key response features, such as mission critical voice capabilities; cybersecurity; and coverage and capacity issues in urban and rural areas. These and other challenges are currently being addressed by multiple entities across all levels of government, academia, and the private sector. As such, public and private sector entities conducting research, development, testing, and evaluation activities should increase collaboration to achieve maximum benefits for emergency responders and ensure that the systems and devices used by public safety are keeping pace with technological change.

Objectives and Recommendations

The National Emergency Communications Plan aims to increase collaboration of research, development, testing, and evaluation activities across all levels of government, as well as include participation from academia, the private sector, and the public safety community, including associations such as the Association of Public-Safety Communications Officials – International and the National Emergency Number Association. The recommendations in this section seek to facilitate the development and use of new mission critical technologies, fulfill emergency responders' broadband needs and requirements, and foster integration and avoid duplication of efforts.

OBJECTIVE 5.1: Ensure a coordinated Federal strategic approach to public safety communications research, development, testing, and

evaluation. Many Federal departments and agencies sponsor research, development, testing, and evaluation programs for public safety communications. Increasing coordination across these programs can help integrate common efforts, improve overall decision-making, establish common expectations and priorities for users and applications, and coordinate investments for products and applications being developed for both Land Mobile Radio and broadband technologies.

Recommendations:

- **Coordinate Federal research and development priorities and user requirements through the Emergency Communications Preparedness Center.** The Emergency Communications Preparedness Center Research and Development Focus Group and Broadband Focus Group should serve as forums for Federal departments and agencies to coordinate communications- related research and development programs, share information with the public safety community, and facilitate short- and long-term research and development planning efforts to ensure programs and activities are aligned with emergency responder needs. In addition, these groups should collect Federal user and service requirements for the Nationwide Public Safety Broadband Network and provide them to the First Responder Network Authority.

- **Increase collaboration between Federal research and development and technology transfer programs across the homeland security, defense, and national security communities.** The homeland security, defense, and national security communities have significant experience developing innovative mobile solutions for agents in the field. For example, the Department of Defense has developed a *Mobile Device Strategy* and *Mobile Applications Security Requirements Guide* focused on improving wireless infrastructure, mobile devices, and mobile applications.[52] Increasing collaboration between defense and public safety research and development programs can help maximize resources on issues that cross disciplines. Potential areas of collaboration include leveraging lessons learned and best practices, identifying areas for partnerships (e.g., application development, or application and user device security), and sharing intellectual property, as appropriate.

OBJECTIVE 5.2: Accelerate the development and adoption of mission critical communication products, applications, and services. The public safety community's adoption of Internet Protocol-enabled communications capabilities will depend on networks, services, security, and applications that meet its needs and requirements. To determine the benefits and expedite the availability and adoption of these products and services, public safety organizations must have detailed requirements, effective solutions, operational testing, and intuitive interfaces so that users can easily deploy solutions in the field with predictable performance. Government research and development programs should engage with private industry-driven research and development efforts—including those within the communications and information technology sectors—to capture the innovation and advancements available in the commercial marketplace.

Accelerating Broadband Infrastructure Deployment

As part of the effort to facilitate wired and wireless broadband infrastructure deployment, the Office of Science and Technology Policy has developed an interactive broadband mapping tool that allows carriers and communities to view and identify opportunities to leverage Federal properties for the deployment of high-speed Internet networks. This data can help the wireless industry make informed project implementation and scheduling decisions.

Recommendations:

- **Foster collaborative mission critical voice, data, and cybersecurity research, development, testing, and evaluation.** As communications technologies migrate to Internet Protocol-based networks, government and academic research facilities should identify and develop new technologies that address public safety mission critical voice and data requirements that are not currently offered by commercial solutions. Identifying and developing these technologies will require coordination with the public safety community through entities such as SAFECOM, the National Public Safety Telecommunications Council, the First Responder Network Authority, and the First Responder Network Authority's Public Safety Advisory Committee.[53] To improve and enhance the security of emergency communications networks and devices, DHS should coordinate with the public safety community to assess and mitigate cyber threats and risks.

- **Government research facilities should facilitate the integration of Next Generation 9-1-1 into a nationwide solution.** Government research facilities should leverage requirements, lessons learned, and best practices from Next Generation 9-1-1 early adopters to spur nationwide deployment and adoption. Researchers should give special consideration to understanding: (1) how Next Generation 9-1-1 networks will interface with the Nationwide Public Safety Broadband Network; (2) potential security risks presented by the use of data between Public Safety Answering Points, Public Safety Communications Centers, and emergency responders; and (3) other potential functions Public Safety Answering Points and Public Safety Communications Centers can leverage in an Internet Protocol-centric environment.

- **Cultivate an innovative marketplace for applications and technologies through the use of public and private partnerships.** In coordination with the First Responder Network Authority and members of the public safety community—including the Public Safety Advisory Committee, SAFECOM, the National Public Safety Telecommunications Council, and the Association of Public-Safety Communications Officials—the Federal Government should proactively engage with application developers to create and maintain mobile applications and products for public safety. The expanding mobile applications marketplace should be used as a model to bring commercial innovation to emergency communications. Many public safety agencies are already collaborating with the applications community to develop unique applications for their localities; however, long-term growth and adoption is predicated on coordination among developers, users, and service providers to ensure that applications are readily available and tailored to public safety needs (including inputs on user needs, bandwidth, and capacity constraints). This includes coordinating on security and privacy issues, as well as the management of sensitive data.

- **Support the evolution of alert and warning systems that deliver timely, relevant, and accessible emergency information to the public.** The emergence of location-based services, mobile video, social media, and other applications offers new opportunities for government agencies and officials to transmit alert and warning messages to the public. To improve the adoption and use of emergency alerting capabilities, such as the Wireless Emergency Alert Program, DHS should continue research, development, testing, and evaluation activities for potential solutions to enhance the geo-targeting precision of message content and delivery. As usage and adoption of Wireless Emergency Alert Program continues to increase, DHS should take advantage of opportunities for increased stakeholder feedback (including vendors, academic partners, and individuals with access and functional needs) to identify gaps, needs, and new technological capabilities that could be integrated into the Wireless Emergency Alert Program roadmap to improve performance and response.

OBJECTIVE 5.3: Modernize communications standards and programs to keep pace with technological change. The Project 25 suite of standards and DHS' priority service programs support interoperability and communications continuity for the public safety community.[54] As new standards and infrastructures are developed, these programs must evolve to meet changing demands and technologies. The Office for Interoperability and Compatibility and the Public Safety Communications Research Program should collaborate with the private sector and participate in standards development organizations to ensure that public safety capabilities are incorporated into current and emerging standards.

Recommendations:

- **Update priority service programs to successfully migrate to Internet Protocol-enabled fixed and mobile broadband networks.** DHS should continue to partner with Federal departments and agencies and communications service providers to ensure that priority service offerings keep pace with commercial deployment of Internet Protocol networks, while at the same time consider priority requirements for the Nationwide Public Safety Broadband Network. This approach should generate: (1) a baseline understanding of current program capabilities and gaps; (2) an analysis of user needs and desired end-state, including any differences from authorized user requirements; (3) a gap analysis of customer needs/end-state and existing offerings; (4) a technology roadmap for priority services; and (5) a resource and timeline estimate to build and implement service offerings based on the gap analysis, as well as technologies from the technology roadmap, including lifecycle costs and timeframes.

- **Increase use and awareness of the Project 25 Compliance Assessment Program.** The Project 25 Compliance Assessment Program was created by the Office for Interoperability and Compatibility, in partnership with the Public Safety Communications Research Program, to help the emergency response community make informed purchasing decisions by providing manufacturers with a method to ensure their equipment complies with Project 25 standards.[55] The Office for Interoperability and Compatibility is transitioning compliance assessment to third-party laboratory accreditation organizations. DHS should continue to release summary test reports and Suppliers' Declaration of Compliance documentation to the public safety community. DHS should also encourage Federal agencies purchasing Project 25 communications equipment to use the resources made available by Project 25 Compliance Assessment Program.

- **Continue to support Project 25 standards development for interoperability.** With the recognition that mission critical voice communications are the primary means of communications for public safety agencies, the emergency response community should continue its commitment to further develop the Project 25 suite of standards for enhanced interoperability. DHS, as the senior Federal partner in the Project 25 standards development process and the chair of the Project 25 Steering Committee, continues to help drive interoperability testing, the addition of enhanced security features, and support for future communications capabilities such as Project 25 to long-term evolution interfaces.

4.0. IMPLEMENTING AND MEASURING THE NATIONAL EMERGENCY COMMUNICATIONS PLAN

The goals, objectives, and recommendations in Section 3.0 provide the blueprint to enhance emergency communications capabilities nationwide, consistent with the National Emergency Communications Plan's legislative requirements. This section reviews DHS' strategy for implementing and measuring the National Emergency Communications Plan in coordination with the Plan's stakeholders. As shown in Exhibit 4, this strategy is driven by a repeatable process that the first National Emergency Communications Plan established to guide emergency communications planning at all levels of government. This strategic management process aims to drive continuous improvement of the Nation's emergency communications capabilities through four primary phases.[56]

- **Analyze:** Assess implementation of existing planning priorities in conjunction with lessons learned from real-world incidents, events, and exercises to identify areas for continued improvement.
- **Develop:** Based on the analysis, generate new strategic priorities (e.g., vision, goals, objectives, and recommendations) to target current gaps and address future needs.
- **Implement:** Design supporting activities and timeframes for achieving the recommendations and building capability.
- **Measure:** Regularly assess progress in meeting milestones and achieving goals.

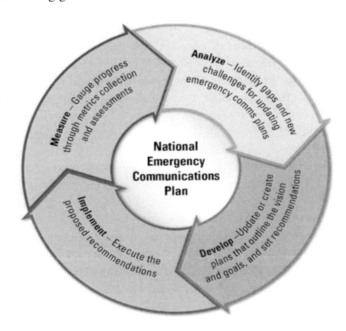

Exhibit 4. National Emergency Communications Plan Strategic Management Process.

4.1. Implementation and Measurement

Although DHS leads the development and management of the National Emergency Communications Plan, the implementation is a shared responsibility among the Department and the Plan's stakeholders. This reflects the nature of the emergency communications community, which spans disciplines, jurisdictions, and levels of government, and also involves the public and private sectors.[57]

The ability of responders to communicate and share information to save lives and protect property is both the most important and most challenging criteria by which to measure the National Emergency Communications Plan's success. Given the multitude of public safety agencies across the Nation—and the large number of incidents to which they respond on a daily basis—consistently evaluating how well communications function during response operations is a major challenge that requires cooperation at all levels of government.

To address this difficult task, DHS partnered with public safety agencies and emergency responders following the release of the 2008 National Emergency Communications Plan to develop an assessment program. This collaboration produced a targeted measurement process based on operational performance benchmarks that enabled jurisdictions to test their capacity to communicate during responses. As a result, more than 2,800 counties or county-equivalents participated in the assessment—including thousands of Federal, State, local, tribal, and territorial agencies. The assessment increased their understanding of how responders coordinate, execute, and communicate during real-world incidents, exercises, or planned events.[58]

The measurement process also allowed jurisdictions to gain a baseline understanding of their emergency communications capabilities, such as the degree to which training and exercises are conducted within a county or county-equivalent. Capability measures were used in combination with operational performance measures to provide a more complete understanding of emergency communications. In general, jurisdictions with higher overall capability measurements can be expected to demonstrate greater operational effectiveness.

DHS will follow this proven approach to measure the progress of this National Emergency Communications Plan. Specifically, the Plan will focus its assessment actions around the following three measures, displayed in Exhibit 5.

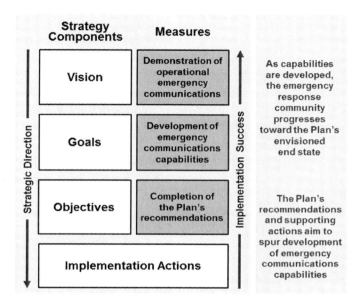

Exhibit 5. National Emergency Communications Plan Measures of Success.

- **Demonstration of operational emergency communications.** To measure progress toward the National Emergency Communications Plan's vision, DHS will employ the same methods for testing operational performance that were used to measure interoperability under the 2008 National Emergency Communications Plan.[59] DHS will partner with jurisdictions across the country to test their ability to demonstrate response-level communications during an incident or event. This includes working with Federal, State, local, tribal, and territorial agencies on appropriate timeframes and benchmarks for these assessments. Also, as broadband technologies and a potentially broader set of stakeholders take a greater role in response and recovery operations, DHS will work with partners to update the performance criteria, as appropriate.
- **Development of emergency communications capabilities.** In addition to operational performance, DHS will assess progress in building emergency communications capabilities consistent with the *SAFECOM Interoperability Continuum*. Developing these capabilities (e.g., governance; policies, practices, and procedures; technology; training and exercises; and usage) is the foundation of a jurisdiction's ability to consistently achieve operational communications at an

incident. The National Emergency Communications Plan capability assessment was a nationwide initiative that helped inform the strategic goals and objectives for the 2014 National Emergency Communications Plan. To measure progress since the last assessment, the Office of Emergency Communications will work with stakeholders across all levels of government to establish targets for their capability levels based on remaining challenges and new developments in the operating environment.

- **Completion of National Emergency Communications Plan recommendations and implementation actions.** The National Emergency Communications Plan goals, objectives, and recommendations aim to drive capability improvements at all levels of government. DHS will partner with National Emergency Communications Plan stakeholders to identify specific activities to support implementation of the Plan's recommendations. Completion of the recommendations will help gauge progress toward achieving the goals and objectives, which in turn help build emergency communications capabilities across the Nation.

4.2. Planning and Reporting

The National Emergency Communications Plan's three-pronged measurement process will generate detailed results on progress and provide a basis for formulating priorities and strategies for future planning. States, territories, urban areas, localities, and tribes are encouraged to leverage their operational and capabilities data for integration into Threat and Hazard Identification and Risk Assessments. DHS will work with its partners at the Federal, State, local, tribal, and territorial levels to analyze results, understand correlations between performance and capability data points, and assess implications for future decision-making.

The National Emergency Communications Plan's results will also help DHS and the Federal Government better target ongoing support for emergency communications, including training, technical assistance, grant guidance, planning assistance, and stakeholder coordination. To ensure awareness, the Office of Emergency Communications will provide regular updates to the stakeholder community on the status of the National Emergency Communications Plan implementation. This outreach effort will allow stakeholders to track their partners' progress, share implementation best practices, and adopt remediation actions, as needed. In addition, the Office of Emergency Communications will provide Congress with progress on the National Emergency Communications Plan's implementation in its *Biennial Progress Report.*[60]

5.0. CONCLUSION

Since 2008, tremendous progress has been made to enhance emergency responder communications capabilities. However, as the emergency communications ecosystem continues to evolve, the Nation must build on previous successes and pursue opportunities for improvement. The 2014 National Emergency Communications Plan emphasizes the close collaboration by stakeholders to plan for and shape the future of emergency communications. The deployment of new technologies provides emergency responders access to high-speed and cutting-edge capabilities, while current emergency communications networks offer responders the security, reliability, and coverage they need to execute their mission in an all-hazards environment. Striking the right balance between addressing existing gaps and requirements while also integrating new technologies is a significant challenge facing public safety organizations across all levels of government.

To that end, the National Emergency Communications Plan sets forth five strategic goals to advance the capabilities needed for operational success in an increasingly dynamic and interconnected environment. The Plan establishes a series of targeted objectives that address each goal and collectively emphasize the maintenance and improvement of Land Mobile Radio systems, preparation for the integration of emerging technologies, and improved coordination among an expanding emergency response community. The Plan identifies actionable recommendations for stakeholders to enhance and update the policies, governance structures, planning, and protocols that enable responders to communicate and share information under all circumstances. Ultimately, the intent of the National Emergency Communications Plan is to ensure the emergency response community drives toward a commonly defined end-state for communications.

Moving forward, emergency response agencies will be making critical decisions regarding resources, personnel, and equipment to address the evolving operating environment. The guidance provided in this Plan will help to advance their efforts. However, success of the Plan will require the support and dedication of the entire emergency communications community, including Federal, State, local, tribal, and territorial partners, nongovernmental organizations, the private sector, and the public. In order to realize the Plan's vision, and help bring public safety communications into the 21st century, DHS and the Office of Emergency Communications will work diligently to ensure that our Nation's emergency responders can fulfill their mission needs in a seamless and fully interoperable next generation communications ecosystem.

APPENDIX 1. STATUTORY REQUIREMENTS MATRIX

6 USC § 572 Requirements	National Emergency Communications Plan Sections
1 Include recommendations developed in consultation with the Federal Communications Commission and the National Institute of Standards and Technology for a process for expediting national voluntary consensus standards for interoperable emergency communications equipment	• Section 3.0 – Objectives 1.3 and 5.3 • Appendix 6
2 Identify the appropriate capabilities necessary for emergency response providers and relevant government officials to continue to communicate in the event of natural disasters, acts of terrorism, and other man-made disasters	• Section 2.0 • Section 3.0 – Objectives 1.2, 2.3, 4.1, 4.3, and 5.3 • Section 4.0 • Appendices 6 and 8
3 Identify the appropriate interoperable emergency communications capabilities necessary for Federal, State, local, and tribal governments in the event of natural disasters, acts of terrorism, and other man-made disasters	• Section 2.0 • Section 3.0 – Objectives 1.2, 1.3, 4.1, and 4.3; • Appendices 6 and 8
4 Recommend both short-term and long-term solutions for ensuring that emergency response providers and relevant government officials can continue to communicate in the event of natural disasters, acts of terrorism, and other man-made disasters	• Section 3.0 – Objectives 1.2, 1.3, 2.3, 3.3, 4.3, 5.2, and 5.3

6 USC § 572 Requirements		National Emergency Communications Plan Sections
5	Recommend both short-term and long-term solutions for deploying interoperable emergency communications systems for Federal, State, local, and tribal governments throughout the Nation, including through the provision of existing and emerging technologies	• Section 3.0 –Objectives 1.3, 2.2, 3.1, 5.1, 5.2, and 5.3
6	Identify how Federal departments and agencies that respond to natural disasters, acts of terrorism, and other man-made disasters can work effectively with State, local, and tribal governments in all States, and with other entities	• Section 3.0 – Objectives 1.1, 1.2, 1.3, 2.1, 2.2, 3.1, 3.2, 3.3, 4.1, and 4.2
7	Identify obstacles to deploying interoperable emergency communications capabilities nationwide and recommend short-term and long-term measures to overcome those obstacles, including recommendations for multi-jurisdictional coordination among Federal, State, local, and tribal governments	• Section 2.0 • Section 3.0, Objectives 1.1, 2.1, 2.2, 2.3, 3.1, 3.2, 3.3, 4.1, 4.2, and 5.2
8	Recommend goals and time frames for the deployment of emergency, command-level communications systems and develop a timetable for the deployment of interoperable emergency communications systems nationwide	• Section 3.0
9	Recommend appropriate measures that emergency response providers should employ to ensure continued operation of relevant governmental communications infrastructure	• Section 3.0 – Objectives 1.1, 1.2, 1.3, 2.3, 3.3, 4.1, 4.3, and 5.3 • Appendices 6 and 8
10	(House Resolution 1) Set a date, including interim benchmarks, by which State, local, and tribal governments, and Federal agencies expect to achieve a baseline level of national interoperable communications	• Section 4.0 • Appendices 6 and 8

APPENDIX 2. KEY AUTHORITIES AND REFERENCES

This appendix provides an overview of the key authorities that guide the development, implementation, and management of the National Emergency Communications Plan. Title XVIII of the *Homeland Security Act of 2002*, as amended, requires the Department of Homeland Security (DHS) to establish and periodically update the National Emergency Communications Plan to guide improvements in emergency communications nationwide.[61] This law and other related statutory actions have helped define improvements to emergency communications. Table A2-1 describes the core set of statutory provisions that provides the foundation for the execution of emergency communications functions.

While this appendix includes the primary authorities that most directly impact emergency communications, there are other key homeland security doctrine and plans that influence the development and implementation of the National Emergency Communications Plan. These plans— including the *National Planning Frameworks*, the *National Infrastructure Protection Plan*, and the *National Incident Management System*—are discussed in Appendix 3, *Part of a Broader National Preparedness Strategy*. The National Emergency Communications Plan is also consistent with, and supports, the DHS 2014 Quadrennial Homeland Security Review, which provides a strategic framework to guide the activities of participants in homeland security towards the goal of a secure and resilient Nation.[62]

Table A2-1. Statutes (in chronological order)

Title	Date Enacted	Description
The Communications Act of 1934, as amended (Title 47 United States Code §151 *et. seq.*)	1934	Regulates interstate and foreign communications by wire and radio in the public interest. Establishes the Federal Communications Commission as the chief regulatory authority on communications matters. Assigns war powers to the President, thereby enabling the Executive Branch of the Federal Government to direct priority provisioning of telecommunications services deemed critical to national security interests during wartime emergencies.

Title	Date Enacted	Description
The Robert T. Stafford Disaster Relief and Emergency Assistance Act, (Title 42 United States Code § 101 *et. seq.*)	1988	Describes the programs and processes by which the Federal Government provides disaster and emergency assistance to State and local governments, tribal nations, eligible private nonprofit organizations, and individuals affected by a declared major disaster or emergency. Establishes the use of temporary communications systems in anticipation of or during an emergency. Applies to response and recovery from all hazards.
The Homeland Security Act of 2002 (Title 6 United States Code § 101 *et. seq.*)	2002	Establishes DHS as an executive department of the United States Government and specifies significant responsibilities associated with emergency preparedness, response, and recovery, including emergency communications. Includes provisions for improving the management, coordination, and interoperability of communications services in support of Federal, State, local, tribal, and territorial authorities.
The Intelligence Reform and Terrorism Prevention Act (Title 42 United States Code § 2000ee, 50 United States Code § 403-1 *et. seq.*, § 403-3 *et. seq.*, § 4040 *et. seq.*)	2004	Acting on recommendations made by the National Commission on Terrorist Attacks Upon the United States (9/11 Commission), strengthens the emergency communications provisions codified by the *Homeland Security Act*. Authorizes the Secretary of Homeland Security to establish a comprehensive national approach to achieving public safety interoperable communications at all levels of government. Establishes the Office for Interoperability and Compatibility to enhance public safety interoperable communications.
The Fiscal Year 2007 Department of Homeland Security Appropriations Act	2006	Includes Title VI, the *Post-Katrina Emergency Management Reform Act*, which reorganizes the Federal Emergency Management Agency, amends the *Stafford Act*, and addresses emergency communications through Subtitle D—The *21ˢᵗ Century Emergency Communications Act of 2006*. The latter amends the *Homeland*

Table A2-1. (Continued)

Title	Date Enacted	Description
		Security Act of 2002 by adding Title XVIII—*Emergency Communications*, which establishes the Office of Emergency Communications, transfers existing programs and functions to the Office, and assigns new responsibilities for developing and implementing a comprehensive national approach to achieving public safety interoperable communications. This includes 6 United States Code § 572 requirements for developing and periodically updating the National Emergency Communications Plan.
Security and Accountability for Every Port Act	2006	Includes Title VI—Commercial Mobile Service Alerts of the *Warning, Alert, and Response Network Act*, which establishes standards, protocols, procedures, other technical requirements and associated Federal Communications Commission (FCC) rules that enable Commercial Mobile Service providers to voluntarily transmit emergency alerts to subscribers. Establishes the Commercial Mobile Service Alert Advisory Committee to develop and submit recommendations to the FCC regarding the technical standards and protocols required for transmitting emergency alerts to subscribers. Amends the *Robert T. Stafford Disaster Relief and Emergency Assistance Act* to define "essential service provider" as a municipal, nonprofit, or private, for profit entity that provides telecommunications service, electrical power, natural gas, water and sewer services, or any other essential service (as determined by the President).
Implementing the Recommendations of the 9/11 Commission Act	2007	Amends the *Homeland Security Act* and other statutes to improve communications for emergency responders through grant programs. Provisions include directing the Secretary of Homeland Security to establish

Title	Date Enacted	Description
		the Interoperable Emergency Communications Grant Program to help States to implement initiatives to improve international, national, regional, statewide, local, and tribal interoperable emergency communications; and establish the Border Interoperability Demonstration Project to facilitate emergency communications across international borders.
The Middle Class Tax Relief and Jobs Creation Act (47 United States Code § 1424 et. seq.)	**2012**	Establishes the First Responder Network Authority, an independent entity within the Federal Government, to ensure the building, deployment and operation of a Nationwide Public Safety Broadband Network to enhance the ability of emergency responders to communicate. Reallocates the 700 megahertz D Block spectrum for public safety use and provides $7 billion in Federal funding toward the deployment of Nationwide Public Safety Broadband Network. The Board governing the First Responder Network Authority is comprised of three permanent members—the Secretary of Homeland Security, the Attorney General, and the Director of the Office of Management and Budget—and 12 term-limited individuals appointed by the Secretary of Commerce.

Table A2-2 describes related executive orders and presidential directives that affect the development and implementation of the National Emergency Communications Plan. These authorities set national policy and provide executive direction in areas closely related to emergency communications, including, but not limited to, national preparedness, domestic incident management, critical infrastructure resilience, cybersecurity, and continuity of government operations. Many of the National Emergency Communications Plan's concepts and strategies align to, intersect with, or are shaped by these authorities.

Table A2-2. Executive Orders and Presidential Directives

Title	Date Issued	Description
Homeland Security Presidential Directive –5, Management of Domestic Incidents	2003	Seeks to enhance management of domestic incidents by establishing a single, comprehensive *National Incident Management System* and developing a *National Response Plan*. (Effective March 22, 2008, the first edition of the *National Response Framework* superseded the *National Response Plan*; the second edition of the *National Response Framework* was issued May 2012). Provides that Federal departments and agencies require States and local entities to adopt the *National Incident Management System*, to the extent permitted by law, for providing Federal preparedness assistance. Identifies the Secretary of Homeland Security as the principal Federal official for domestic incident management.
Executive Order 13407, Public Alert and Warning System	2006	Directs the Department of Homeland Security to oversee the development of an effective, reliable, integrated, flexible, and comprehensive system to alert and warn the American people and to ensure that the President can communicate with the public under all conditions.
National Security Presidential Directive– 51/Homeland Security Policy Directive–20, National Continuity Policy	2007	Establishes a comprehensive national policy on the continuity of Federal Government structures and operations. Prescribes continuity requirements for all Executive Branch departments and agencies, and provides guidance for State, local, tribal, and territorial governments, and private sector organizations to enable a more rapid and effective response to and recovery from a national emergency. Directs the Secretary of Homeland Security to develop, implement, and maintain a comprehensive continuity communications architecture.
Presidential Policy Directive– 8, National Preparedness	2011	Seeks to strengthen the security and resilience of the United States through systematic preparation for threats that pose the greatest risk to the Nation's security. Directs the Secretary of Homeland Security to oversee the development of the *National Preparedness Goal, National*

Title	Date Issued	Description
		Preparedness System, National Preparedness Report, and a Campaign for Building and Sustaining Preparedness. Emphasizes that national preparedness is the shared responsibility of the whole community. Replaces Homeland Security Policy Directive-8, *National Preparedness.*
Executive Order13618, Assignment of National Security and Emergency Preparedness Communications Functions	2012	Assigns national security and emergency preparedness communications functions to Federal Government entities to ensure the Executive Branch can communicate at all times and under all circumstances to carry out its most critical and time sensitive missions. Establishes an interagency National Security and Emergency Preparedness Communications Executive Committee to serve as a forum to address national security and emergency preparedness communications matters. Revokes Executive Order 12472, *Assignment of National Security and Emergency Preparedness Telecommunications Functions*, thereby decommissioning the National Communications System.
Presidential Policy Directive– 21, Critical Infrastructure Security and Resilience	2013	Addresses the roles and responsibilities across the Federal Government and establishes a more effective partnership with critical infrastructure owners and operators and State, local, tribal, and territorial entities to enhance the security and resilience of critical infrastructure. Replaces Homeland Security Policy Directive- 7, *Critical Infrastructure Identification, Prioritization, and Protection.*

APPENDIX 3. PART OF A BROADER PREPAREDNESS STRATEGY

The Nation continues to develop and implement strategies to strengthen preparedness and resiliency in the midst of a dynamic threat environment. These efforts have yielded the *National Incident Management System*;

National Preparedness Goal; *National Preparedness System*; National Planning Frameworks; and a coordinated National Exercise Program. Working together, these components help the Nation develop and deliver the core capabilities identified in the Goal, including operational communications.

As a strategic plan for emergency communications, the National Emergency Communications Plan is a key component in this portfolio. This appendix describes how the National Emergency Communications Plan aligns with, implements, and supports our Nation's broader national preparedness strategy.

Presidential Policy Directive - 8

Signed by the President in March 2011, Presidential Policy Directive-8, *National Preparedness*, is aimed at strengthening the security and resilience of the United States through systematic preparation for the threats that pose the greatest risk to the security of the Nation.[63] It consists of four main components: the *National Preparedness Goal*; *National Preparedness System*; *National Preparedness Report*; and the Campaign to Build and Sustain Preparedness. The directive emphasizes that national preparedness is the shared responsibility of the whole community.

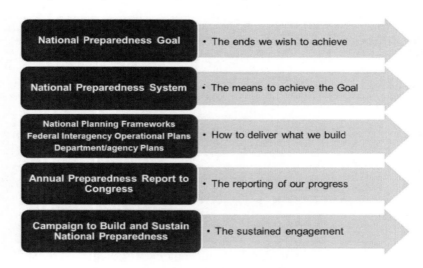

Exhibit A3-1. Key Components of Presidential Policy Directive-8.

As technologies have evolved and responsibilities have expanded to include more nongovernmental partners, the National Emergency Communications Plan recognizes that engaging a broad set of stakeholders is critical to effective information sharing and communications during emergencies. The following section offers additional detail on the National Emergency Communications Plan's relationship to the elements of Presidential Policy Directive-8:

- **National Preparedness Goal:** The *National Preparedness Goal* is the cornerstone for the implementation of Presidential Policy Directive-8. It establishes the capabilities and outcomes for the Nation to accomplish across all five mission areas (Prevention, Protection, Mitigation, Response, and Recovery) in order to be secure and resilient. Each of the five mission areas has distinct core capabilities and corresponding target elements necessary for success. While the majority of the National Emergency Communications Plan's proposed recommendations support the Response mission area and the operational communications core capability identified in the Goal, many of the Plan's goals and objectives also foster planning and coordination across the Prevention, Protection, Mitigation, and Recovery mission areas.
- **National Preparedness System:** The *National Preparedness System* is the methodology through which the Goal is implemented. The System consists of six components: (1) identifying and assessing risk; (2) estimating the level of capabilities needed to address those risks; (3) building or sustaining the required levels of capability; (4) developing and implementing plans to deliver those capabilities; (5) validating and monitoring progress; and (6) reviewing and updating efforts to promote continuous improvement. The National Emergency Communications Plan has incorporated all six of these components as they pertain to emergency communications. In particular, the National Emergency Communications Plan's strategic management process, identified in Section 4.0, provides a consistent and repeatable approach to support planning, decision-making, resource allocation, and measuring progress toward building, maintaining, and sustaining capabilities. Specific linkages between the National Emergency Communications Plan and other key components of the Preparedness System include:

- *Identifying and Assessing Risk and Estimating Capability Requirements:* As discussed in Section 2.0 of the National Emergency Communications Plan, public safety officials will need to prepare for the increasing security risks to the emergency communications architecture. This includes, but is not limited to, threats to open architecture and Internet-based technologies and services; security risks presented by data sharing between Public Safety Answering Points, Public Safety Communications Centers, and first responders; and cyber risks. The Threat and Hazard Identification and Risk Assessment process provides a common, consistent approach for identifying and assessing risks and associated impacts. It builds on existing State, local, tribal, and territorial hazard identification and risk assessments. Jurisdictions can integrate the findings from the National Emergency Communications Plan assessment process into their Threat and Hazard Identification and Risk Assessments, which can ultimately provide them with a better understanding of overall communications gaps. This can support more informed decision-making on resource allocation, operations planning, and mitigation activities.
- *Building and Sustaining Capabilities.* Building and sustaining capabilities is a key output of the National Emergency Communications Plan. The Plan's recommendations aim to increase emergency communications capabilities through responders' proficiency with communications equipment, as well as training, planning, coordination, and education.
- *Validating Capabilities.* Exercises, remedial action management programs, and assessments are some of the methods to validate capabilities. Effective training and exercise programs can bolster emergency responders' proficiency with communications equipment, as well as improve their ability to execute policies, plans, and procedures governing the use of communications. The National Emergency Communications Plan emphasizes the need to enhance responders' ability to coordinate and communicate through training and exercises, as well as assessing capabilities on a regular basis.

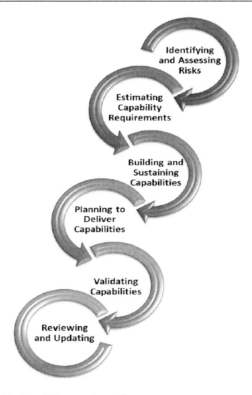

Exhibit A3-2. The National Preparedness System.

- **National Planning System.** The *National Planning System*, part of the *National Preparedness System*, provides a unified system with a common terminology and approach, built around plans that support the all-threats and -hazards approach to preparedness. These plans—whether strategic, operational, or tactical—enable the whole community to build, sustain, and deliver the core capabilities identified in the *National Preparedness Goal*. The National Emergency Communications Plan helps implement several key pieces of the *National Planning System*, including:
  - *National Response Framework.* The *National Response Framework*, one of five national planning frameworks, is a guide for how the Nation responds to all types of disasters and emergencies. It identifies roles, responsibilities, and coordinating

structures for incident response and provides the structure and mechanisms to execute national-level policy and support for incident management. As such, the National Emergency Communications Plan aligns to the principles and constructs of the *National Response Framework* by providing policy and planning guidance that supports the response core capabilities, namely operational communications.

> **Operational Communications Core Capability**
>
> Ensure the capacity for timely communications in support of security, situational awareness, and operations by any and all means available, among and between affected communities in the impact area and all response forces.

- *Federal Interagency Operational Plans.* The *Federal Interagency Operational Plans* for each mission area further define the concepts, principles, structures, and actions introduced in their respective frameworks, with a specific focus on these elements at the Federal level. The *Response Federal Interagency Operational Plan* is the plan to which the National Emergency Communications Plan is most directly associated, as it addresses specific tasks for the operational communications core capability. The National Emergency Communications Plan's goals and recommendations aim to support Federal partners in executing tasks pertaining to the operational communications core capability.
- *Departmental Plans.* Any Federal department or agency with responsibility for emergency communications should ensure that its operational plans align to the goals and objectives of the National Emergency Communications Plan. For example, the Department of Homeland Security (DHS) is developing a Department-wide, integrated communications interoperability plan to improve interoperable and emergency communications, including land mobile radio voice integration with broadband data technology.

- **National Preparedness Report.** DHS is required to report annually to Congress on the progress the Nation is making towards building and sustaining the core capabilities. The report is structured around the core capabilities identified in the Goal. As part of the assessment of the operational communications core capability, DHS has and will continue to report on key results from implementation of the National Emergency Communications Plan in the annual *Preparedness Report to Congress.* The *2013 National Preparedness Report to Congress,* for example, includes results from the National Emergency Communications Plan capability assessment. It also credits the National Emergency Communications Plan with helping jurisdictions progress beyond the early stage of interoperable communications development and close numerous communications capability gaps. In addition, the report shows that 92 percent of States and territories rated the operational communications capability as a high priority.[64]

National Incident Management System

Mandated by Homeland Security Presidential Directive- 5, *Management of Domestic Incidents,* the *National Incident Management System* provides a systematic, proactive approach and template to guide departments and agencies at all levels of government, nongovernmental organizations, and the private sector to work seamlessly to prevent, protect against, respond to, recover from, and mitigate the effects of incidents, regardless of cause, size, location, or complexity. First issued in 2004, the *National Incident Management System* establishes a core set of concepts, principles, terminology, and technologies covering the incident command system; multi-agency coordination systems; unified command; training; identification and management of resources (including systems for classifying types of resources); qualifications and certification; and the collection, tracking, and reporting of incident information and incident resources.

To implement the 2008 National Emergency Communications Plan, DHS evaluated jurisdictions' use of the *National Incident Management System* components, concepts, and principles as they related to command, control, and communications. This included assessing the effectiveness and regularity of Incident Command System implementation, namely the performance of responder roles and responsibilities utilizing the Incident Command System command structure; the use of easily- understood language; and the use of

Incident Action Plans and Incident Command System forms. The assessment also reviewed the use of the Operations Section Chief position, which plays a key role in facilitating the exchange of information among agencies and across disciplines, and the Communications Unit Leader, who is responsible for establishing and maintaining communications interoperability for responding agencies. The Office of Emergency Communications will continue to evaluate the implementation of the *National Incident Management System* components, concepts, and principles as they relate to communications as part of the National Emergency Communications Plan performance and capability assessments.

National Infrastructure Protection Plan

The *National Infrastructure Protection Plan* and its 16 sector-specific plans create a system to protect public and privately-owned critical infrastructure. The National Emergency Communications Plan acknowledges the importance of critical infrastructure sectors to the emergency communications ecosystem; not only does it address leveraging and integrating communications services, teams, and capabilities into response operations, it also focuses on the growing interdependencies between the communications and other sectors (e.g., transportation, energy, and health). DHS also worked with the main private sector partnership—the Critical Infrastructure Partnership Advisory Council—to coordinate the communications and emergency services sectors' input for the National Emergency Communications Plan.

APPENDIX 4. ROLES AND RESPONSIBILITIES

This appendix provides an overview of the roles and responsibilities of the key public and private stakeholders who are involved in the emergency communications mission and the implementation of the National Emergency Communications Plan. In addition to emergency responders at all levels of government, this appendix also addresses key private sector and nongovernmental organizations, as well as partnerships and advisory committees, with whom the Federal Government coordinates emergency communications policies, plans, and programs.

All Levels of Government

The responsibility for responding to and managing planned events and incidents begins at the local level—with individuals, first responders, and public officials in the county, city, or town affected by the incident. When emergencies escalate, additional support may be requested from other jurisdictions, States, or even the Federal Government. Operational communications is a core capability for any incident, regardless of size, location, or cause; therefore, each level of government must take the necessary preparedness actions to ensure the capacity to communicate with both the emergency response community and the affected populations, as well as with other governmental entities.

Local Jurisdictions

Local leaders, emergency managers, and public safety officials prepare their communities to manage incidents locally. Among their numerous responsibilities, these officials provide strategic guidance; manage resources; develop and implement policies and budgets; and oversee local preparedness efforts to improve emergency management and response capabilities. A number of local entities involved in response operations require interoperable, continuous, and secure communications to carry out their missions. This includes public safety disciplines, such as local law enforcement, fire, and emergency medical service personnel who respond to the early stages of an incident and are primarily responsible for the protection and preservation of life, property, evidence, and the environment. In addition, emergency management agencies are also involved with coordination and communications during incidents by disseminating alerts and warnings and operating emergency operations centers, among other key functions. Local Public Safety Answering Points and Public Safety Communications Centers also play critical roles by serving as key communications and information conduits between the public and emergency responders. Since natural and man-made emergency response efforts generally begin at the local level, coordination among these entities is critical to ensuring effective communications and information sharing when responding to emergencies of all scopes and sizes.

State Agencies

State agencies and officials help coordinate and integrate statewide responders and resources into the local incident command before, during, and after incidents. States must be prepared to maintain or accelerate the provision of emergency communications resources and services when an incident grows and local capabilities are unable to keep up with demand. Likewise, if a State anticipates that its resources may be exceeded, they must have a process in place to request and integrate Federal assistance. A listing of the key statewide officials and governing bodies with responsibility for emergency communications are described below. This list is not intended to be exhaustive as some States have additional agencies or individuals with whom they interact.[65]

- **Statewide Interoperability Coordinator.** The Statewide Interoperability Coordinators serves as the State's single point of contact for interoperable communications and implements the Statewide Communication Interoperability Plan, which establishes a vision for interoperability in the State.
- **State Single Point of Contact.** The single point of contact serves as the coordinator for the State and Local Implementation Grant Program and First Responder Network Authority's efforts with respect to the Nationwide Public Safety Broadband Network. This person may or may not be the Statewide Interoperability Coordinator.
- **Statewide Interoperability Governing Body or Statewide Interoperability Executive Committee.** The Statewide Interoperability Governing Body or Statewide Interoperability Executive Committee serves as the primary steering group for the statewide interoperability strategy. Its mission is to support the National Council of Statewide Interoperability Coordinators in efforts to improve emergency response communications across the State through enhanced data and voice communications interoperability. Statewide Interoperability Governing Bodies and Statewide Interoperability Executive Committees often include representatives from various jurisdictions, disciplines, as well as subject matter experts.
- **State Emergency Management Agency Director.** The director of the State emergency management agency is responsible for ensuring that the State is prepared to deal with any type of emergency, as well as coordinating statewide incident response. This includes collaborating with appropriate statewide representatives for critical

capabilities, such as emergency communications. The director may also have the responsibility for statewide 9-1-1 communications and public alerting.

- **State Information Technology and Security Officials.** A State or territory's chief information officer, chief technology officer, and chief information security officer manage key information technology and broadband deployment initiatives, including information technology procurement, security, and information technology planning and budgeting.
- **State 9-1-1 Administrator.** This individual manages a State's or territory's 9-1-1 functions as determined by State legislation. The official title and role of this position may vary by State or territory.

Territories

Similar to each State, territorial governments are also responsible for coordinating the emergency communications resources needed to respond to incidents of all types and any scale, determining their resource capacity, and ensuring an efficient process for requesting assistance, when necessary. Given that their geographical locations often present unique challenges for receiving assistance during times of disaster, it is equally important for territorial governments to prioritize emergency communications. It is especially critical for territories to build relationships and partnerships among neighboring islands, other nearby countries, States, the private sector, nongovernmental organizations, and the Federal Government.

Tribal Nations

Indian country is geographically dispersed across the United States, and tribe size varies significantly, both by enrollment and land area. Federal agencies respect tribal self-government and sovereignty, honor tribal treaties and other rights, and strive to meet the responsibilities that arise from the unique legal relationship between the Federal Government and tribal governments. Communications and emergency services might be handled internally by a tribe; provided by Federal, State, or county entities; or handled by any combination thereof. These jurisdictional complexities can greatly complicate emergency response and communications. Many reservations are located in rural areas far from emergency services, which also pose challenges for first responder communications.

Federal Departments and Agencies

The Federal Government has an array of capabilities and resources that can be made available to support emergency response efforts at all levels of government. Federal departments or agencies may function as first responders for incidents involving primary Federal jurisdiction or authorities (e.g., on a military base, a Federal facility, or Federal lands). Under these circumstances, a Federal department or agency becomes the central coordinator of emergency communications activities with State, local, tribal, territorial, and regional partners. Examples include the United States Coast Guard or the Environmental Protection Agency for oil and hazardous materials spills and the United States Forest Service or the Department of the Interior for fires on Federal lands.

Emergency Communications Preparedness Center Members

- Department of Agriculture
- Department of Commerce
- Department of Defense
- Department of Energy
- Department of Health & Human Services
- Department of Homeland Security
- Department of the Interior
- Department of Justice
- Department of Labor
- Department of State
- Department of Transportation
- Department of the Treasury
- Federal Communications Commission
- General Services Administration

At the same time, the Federal Government is responsible for ensuring the efficient delivery of Federal capabilities for large-scale and catastrophic incidents in support of State, local, tribal, and territorial government efforts, as well as other Federal partners. This can include the following communication functions:

- Facilitating Federal, State, local, tribal, and territorial planning through funding, technical assistance, and guidance;
- Promoting the development of national, regional, and statewide communications plans to address how available Federal assets can be incorporated during times of crisis;

- Promoting the alignment of Federal, State, local, tribal, territorial, and private sector emergency communications plans and preparedness activities to facilitate the development of robust regional communications coordination capabilities; and
- Supporting Federal, State, local, tribal, and territorial operational efforts, providing surge capacity and coordinating distribution of Federal resources to support emergency communications.

Private Sector Entities and Nongovernmental Organizations

Private Sector

As the owners and operators of the majority of the Nation's critical infrastructure, private sector entities are responsible for protecting key commercial communications assets, as well as ensuring the resiliency and reliability of communications during day-to-day operations and emergency response and recovery efforts. In addition, commercial communications carriers have a primary role in network restoration during outages and service failures and support reconstitution for emergency response and recovery operations. The communications sector has a history of successfully cooperating both within the sector and with response entities at all levels of government. These relationships help government and the private sector coordinate joint incident response activities, share and analyze infrastructure information, and coordinate standards development and priority service technologies.

> **Private Sector Partnerships**
>
> "Update national strategies (such as the National Response Framework and the National Emergency Communications Plan) and initiatives to account for advanced [Next Generation Network] communications capabilities, such as the Nationwide Public Safety Broadband Network, and to reflect the evolving communications environment."
>
> – National Security Telecommunications Advisory Committee Report to the President on the National Security and Emergency Preparedness Implications of a Nationwide Public Safety Broadband Network

The private sector's extensive experience protecting, restoring, and reconstituting the communications infrastructure will be particularly important as the Nation plans and prepares for the adoption, migration, and use of emerging technologies, including deployment of the Nationwide Public Safety Broadband Network. Its expertise provides insight on how to address network vulnerabilities so that emergency communications are reliable and resilient during times of crisis.

Depending on the type of incident and its scale, other private sector entities may also have a role supporting, facilitating, or using communications during emergencies, as well as provide services and networks for the government to alert the public. For example, key private sector partners— including privately-owned transportation and transit, telecommunications, utilities, financial institutions, hospitals, and other health regulated facilities— may need to establish and maintain a direct line of communication between their organization and emergency response officials.

Nongovernmental Organizations

Nongovernmental organizations can play vital roles during emergency response and recovery operations, as they have the capability to deliver specialized services that support core capabilities, including operational communications.[66] Nongovernmental organizations include voluntary and non-profit organizations that provide shelter, food, and other essential support services and disaster relief.[67] As technology evolves, various s are also implementing new ways to facilitate communications and information sharing during emergencies.

Individuals and Volunteer Organizations

As discussed in Section 2.0 of the National Emergency Communications Plan, the public and volunteer groups play an increasingly important role in emergency communications. Emergencies are often first reported to authorities by members of the public seeking assistance, and—more than ever before— the public is encouraged to alert the government to potentially dangerous or suspicious activities or update officials on the aftermath of an incident. For example, the Department of Homeland Security's (DHS) "If You See Something, Say Something" campaign emphasizes the importance of reporting suspicious activity to the proper local law enforcement authorities.

> **Nongovernmental Organization Communications During Response Operations**
>
> The American Red Cross has established a digital operations center in Washington, D.C., that enables the organization to more effectively understand and anticipate disaster needs in order to deploy assistance more efficiently. The center has the capability to monitor, respond to, and analyze social media platforms, share timely information, coordinate with other emergency response entities, and allocate resources accordingly. The American Red Cross has developed a training program to leverage digital volunteers that can be called upon to scale up digital operations for emergency situations, such as Hurricane Sandy.

Likewise, volunteer organizations such as community emergency response teams and auxiliary communications volunteers (e.g., amateur radio operators; also called Hams) play key roles in emergency communications and preparedness. Volunteer emergency communications operators and groups using amateur radio have been providing backup communications to event planners, public safety officials, and emergency managers at all levels of government for nearly 100 years. Often, amateur radio services have been used when other forms of communications have failed or have been disrupted. Today, nearly all the States and territories have incorporated some level of participation by amateur radio auxiliary communication operators into their Tactical Interoperable Communications Plans and Statewide Communication Interoperability Plans; this allows them to quickly integrate the operators into response efforts, which can strengthen communications and operations during incidents of any scale.

Partnership and Advisory Groups

Partnership groups are key mechanisms for successful implementation of the National Emergency Communications Plan and execution of the national emergency communications mission. They provide best practices and subject matter expertise to the government, and allow emergency response stakeholders to cultivate working relationships and help shape strategic and operational plans to improve emergency communications. With the changes in the emergency communications landscape, as noted in Section 2.0 of the National Emergency Communications Plan, the pool of partnerships and their roles and responsibilities for supporting emergency communications continues to evolve and expand. Table A4-1 includes a listing of key partnership organizations and advisory bodies:

Table A4-1. Emergency Communications Partnerships and Advisory Groups

Group	Description of Roles and Responsibilities
Canada – United States Communications Interoperability Working Group	The Canada – United States Communications Interoperability Working Group is a joint effort between Canada and the United States. It is co-chaired by Public Safety Canada and DHS' Office of Emergency Communications. The Interoperability Working Groups goal is to support each country's national interoperability strategy and work to resolve bilateral issues of common interest concerning cross-border communications and information exchange.
Communications Security, Reliability and Interoperability Council	The Communications Security, Reliability and Interoperability Council is an advisory committee that provides recommendations to the FCC to ensure, among other things, optimal security and reliability of communications systems, including telecommunications, media, and public safety.
Critical Infrastructure Partnership Advisory Council	The Critical Infrastructure Partnership Advisory Council is a DHS program established to facilitate effective coordination of critical infrastructure activities among the Federal Government; the private sector; and State, local, tribal, and territorial governments.
Emergency Communications Preparedness Center	As the Federal interagency focal point for interoperable and operable emergency communications coordination, the Emergency Communications Preparedness Center's mission is to improve emergency communications collaboration across the Federal Government, and align initiatives with national goals, policy, and guidance. The 14 Federal departments and agencies that comprise the

Group	Description of Roles and Responsibilities
	Emergency Communications Preparedness Center represent the Federal Government's broad role in emergency communications, including planning, policy, operations, grants, and technical assistance.
National Council of Statewide Interoperability Coordinators	Comprised of all Statewide Interoperability Coordinators, the National Council of Statewide Interoperability Coordinators assists State and territory interoperability coordinators with promoting the critical importance of interoperable communications and the sharing of best practices to ensure the highest level of interoperable communications across the Nation.
National Public Safety Telecommunications Council	Composed of State and local public safety representatives, the National Public Safety Telecommunications Council is a federation of national public safety leadership organizations dedicated to improving emergency response communications and interoperability through collaborative leadership.
National Security/ Emergency Preparedness Communications Executive Committee	Executive Order 13618, *Assignment of National Security and Emergency Preparedness Communications Functions*, established the National Security and Emergency Preparedness Executive Committee in July 2012 as a forum—comprised of representatives from at least eight designated Federal agencies—to recommend policy and advise the President on national security and emergency preparedness communications issues.
National Security Telecommunications Advisory Committee	The President's National Security Telecommunications Advisory Committee is composed of private sector executives who represent major communications and network service providers, as well as information technology, finance, and aerospace companies. Through DHS, the National Security Telecommunications Advisory Committee provides private sector-based analyses and recommendations to the President and the Executive Branch on policy and enhancements to national security and emergency preparedness communications.

Table A4-1. (Continued)

Group	Description of Roles and Responsibilities
One DHS Emergency Communications Committee	The One DHS Emergency Communications Committee coordinates intra-DHS emergency communications activities and addresses the many challenges facing the Department's emergency communications programs. The committee aligns these efforts and also provides a forum to identify priorities and synergies. It consists of senior officials from the 22 DHS components.
Public Safety Advisory Committee	The Public Safety Advisory Committee is a standing advisory committee that assists the First Responder Network Authority in carrying out its duties and responsibilities. The Public Safety Advisory Committee is comprised of 40 representatives from various public safety organizations that are part of the DHS SAFECOM program.
Regional Emergency Communications Coordination Working Group	The Regional Emergency Communications Coordination Working Groups serve as the single coordination point for emergency communications at the regional level. A Regional Emergency Communications Coordination Working Group has been established in each of the 10 FEMA regions. Each Regional Emergency Communications Coordination Working Group has unique membership dependent on regional government structure and processes.
SAFECOM Executive Committee and Emergency Response Council	SAFECOM is an emergency communications program of the Department of Homeland Security. As a stakeholder-driven program, SAFECOM is led by an Executive Committee, in support of the Emergency Response Council—groups that are primarily composed of State and local emergency responders and intergovernmental and national public safety communications associations. Both groups regularly convene to discuss interoperability, emergency communications, and provide input on the challenges, needs, and best practices of emergency responders. The Office of Emergency Communications develops policy, guidance, and future initiatives by drawing on Executive Committee and Emergency Response Council expertise, best practices, and recommendations.

APPENDIX 5. SAFECOM INTEROPERABILITY CONTINUUM

Developed with practitioner input from the Department of Homeland Security's (DHS) SAFECOM program, the Interoperability Continuum is designed to assist emergency response agencies and policy makers to plan and implement interoperability solutions for data and voice communications. This tool identifies the five critical success elements that must be addressed to achieve a sophisticated interoperability solution: governance, standard operating procedures, technology, training and exercises, and usage of interoperable communications. The Interoperability Continuum can be used by jurisdictions to track progress in strengthening interoperable communications. In addition, the DHS Office of Emergency Communications has used the Interoperability Continuum to develop the priorities and measure the goals of the National Emergency Communications Plan. For more information, see Section 4.0 *Implementing and Measuring the National Emergency Communications Plan.*

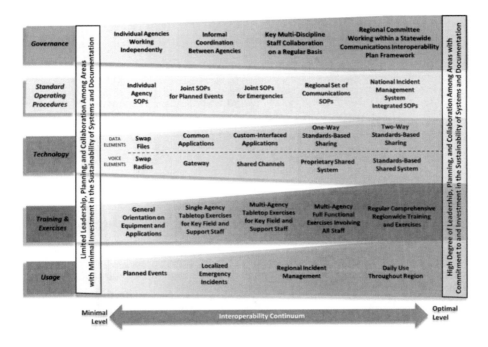

Exhibit A5-1. SAFECOM Interoperability Continuum.

Interoperability is a multi-dimensional challenge. To gain a true picture of a region's interoperability, progress in each of the five interdependent elements must be considered. For example, when a region procures new equipment, that region should plan and conduct training and exercises to maximize the use of that equipment. Optimal level interoperability is contingent upon individual agency and jurisdictional needs. The Continuum is designed as a guide for jurisdictions that are pursuing a new interoperability solution, based on changing needs or additional resources; it is an evolving tool that supports national preparedness doctrine including, but not limited to, the *National Incident Management System*, the *National Response Framework*, and the National Emergency Communications Plan. To maximize the Interoperability Continuum's value to the emergency response community, SAFECOM will regularly update the tool through a consensus process involving practitioners, technical experts, and representatives from Federal, State, local, and tribal agencies.

APPENDIX 6: SUMMARY OF PROGRESS IMPLEMENTING THE 2008 NATIONAL EMERGENCY COMMUNICATIONS PLAN

The 2008 *National Emergency Communications Plan* advanced a more strategic approach to strengthening emergency communications by encouraging emergency response agencies at all levels of government to assess their capabilities and target their activities and resources. The National Emergency Communications Plan established a vision for the desired future state of emergency communications and set performance-based goals to measure progress toward that vision.

The 2008 Plan also included 92 milestones that served as key benchmarks for tracking progress.

This appendix reviews the results of these initiatives and other key achievements to improve emergency communications since publication of the 2008 National Emergency Communications Plan. As depicted in Exhibit A6-1, it is organized around the measures of success as outlined in Section 4.0 of the National Emergency Communications Plan:

- Demonstration of operational emergency communications;
- Development of emergency communications capabilities; and

- Completion of 2008 National Emergency Communications Plan initiatives and recommendations.

Operational Emergency Communications

The National Emergency Communications Plan established the first set of national performance goals to evaluate emergency communications during local emergencies and complex events, as well as a process to measure these goals in every State and territory. The process generated unparalleled data on interoperable emergency communications capabilities and gaps. As a result, the Department of Homeland Security (DHS) and Federal, State, local, tribal, and territorial decision-makers can more effectively evaluate the impact of funding decisions and allocate future resources where they are most needed. The goals of the 2008 Plan were:

- *Goal 1: By 2010, 90 percent of all high-risk urban areas designated within the Urban Areas Security Initiative can demonstrate response-level emergency communications within one hour for routine events involving multiple jurisdictions and agencies.*[68]
- *Goal 2: By 2011, 75 percent of non- Urban Areas Security Initiative jurisdictions can demonstrate response-level emergency communications within one hour for routine events involving multiple jurisdictions and agencies.*
- *Goal 3: By 2013, 75 percent of all jurisdictions are able to demonstrate response-level emergency communications within three hours, in the event of a significant incident as outlined in national planning scenarios.*

To measure the first goal, DHS' Office of Emergency Communications worked with 60 urban areas to assess their ability to demonstrate response-level emergency communications during real-world planned events (e.g., large public gatherings, parades, and sporting events). Based on the capabilities documented at these assessments, all 60 metropolitan areas demonstrated response-level emergency communications in accordance with National Emergency Communications Plan Goal 1. The demonstrations illustrated how the metropolitan areas' organizational and technical investments had improved their respective emergency communications capabilities.[69]

Exhibit A6-1. National Emergency Communications Plan Measures of Success.

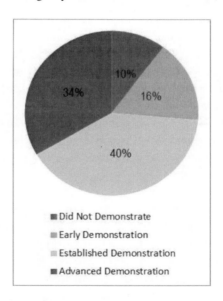

Exhibit A6-2. Operational Performance Assessment Results.

For jurisdictions outside of large metropolitan areas, the Office of Emergency Communications worked with all 56 States and territories to conduct a national assessment of emergency communications capabilities at the county level, including county-equivalents and parishes, municipalities, and townships. The Office of Emergency Communications designed the assessment to help States and territories better understand emergency communications capabilities at the local level, identify where progress is being made, and target resources to address current needs and challenges.

The Statewide Interoperability Coordinators were responsible for coordinating the assessment process with their States' counties, including measuring, collecting, and validating data from local emergencies, including unplanned incidents (e.g., tornadoes, vehicle accidents, missing persons, and earthquakes) or planned events.

States and territories submitted performance reports covering more than 2,800 counties and county-equivalents, which involved 30,000 individual public safety agencies. This represented about 87 percent of the 3,226 jurisdictions that were within the scope of the assessment. Among the jurisdictions that used real-world incidents, about 40 percent of them—or 484 counties—assessed communications performance during natural disasters, including floods, earthquakes, hurricanes, and tornado outbreaks. This effectively satisfied the requirement for the National Emergency Communications Plan Goal 3, as 86 percent of those jurisdictions demonstrated response-level communications during major disasters within three hours. Exhibit A6-2 provides a break-down of the overall results, also summarized below.

- 34 percent of counties demonstrated "Advanced" response-level communications capabilities, meaning that in the reported scenario, the county was generally able to consistently maintain response-level communications during routine incidents and events involving multiple jurisdictions, disciplines, and agencies and would be able to effectively address a significant incident were it to occur.
- 40 percent of counties demonstrated "Established" response-level communications capabilities, meaning that in the reported scenario, the county consistently provided response-level communications during routine incidents and events involving multiple jurisdictions, disciplines, and agencies.
- 16 percent of counties demonstrated "Early" response-level communications capabilities, meaning that in the reported scenario, the county largely used ad hoc communications coordination with few

documented plans or procedures during routine incidents and events involving multiple jurisdictions, disciplines, and agencies.

- 10 percent of counties did not demonstrate any response-level communications capabilities, meaning that in the reported scenario, the county did not demonstrate response- level communications due to a lack of planning, policies, and technical solutions for interoperability areas of emergency communications.

> "This plan [the National Emergency Communications Plan] and other significant Federal efforts represent an increasingly strategic approach by the Federal government to enhance emergency communications and address existing vulnerabilities... Department of Homeland Security (DHS) and other Federal agencies have recently taken significant and strategic steps."
> — **Government Accountability Office,**
> Report GAO-09-604, June 2009

The National Emergency Communications Plan performance assessments clearly showed the progress that jurisdictions have made over the past several years toward establishing interoperable emergency communications during incidents, events, and exercises. It is important to note that for jurisdictions that were able to demonstrate response-level communications, the level of proficiency varied greatly; with this in mind, the Office of Emergency Communications has worked with the States, territories, and jurisdictions to identify gaps through technical assistance, guidance documents, and similar support efforts.

Emergency Communications Capabilities

To assess jurisdictions' emergency communications more broadly, the Office of Emergency Communications requested that counties or equivalents report on their overall communications capabilities that align to the elements of the *SAFECOM Interoperability Continuum*.[70] For comparison purposes, the Office of Emergency Communications designed the capability assessments to closely mirror the 2006 SAFECOM National Interoperability Baseline Survey. The survey results revealed progress in several key areas, including:

- **Governance:** The percentage of jurisdictions involved in formal decision-making groups and strategic planning for emergency communications had doubled.
- **Standard Operating Procedures:** The percentage of jurisdictions with formal interoperability standard operating procedures —meaning procedures that are published and activated during incident response—increased from 51 percent to 86 percent of respondents.
- **Use of Interoperable Communications:** The capability results showed that the percentage of jurisdictions that regularly achieve interoperability had increased from 65 percent to 84 percent of respondents in 2011.

Exhibit A6-3 shows the overall capability results across four lanes of the *SAFECOM Interoperability Continuum*. The Office of Emergency Communications and the States have used the data collected through the performance reports in combination with capability data to develop a more complete understanding of emergency communications across the Nation. In general, the results showed that those counties that demonstrated response-level communications had higher overall capability results than those counties that did not demonstrate the goal.

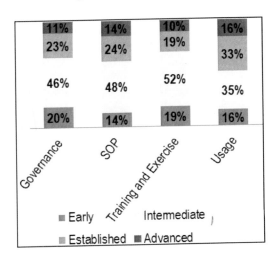

Exhibit A6-3. Capability Results.

Achievement of National Emergency Communications Plan Initiatives and Milestones

The 2008 National Emergency Communications Plan includes seven objectives intended to close existing capability gaps and achieve the document's long-term vision. In addition, the Plan included supporting initiatives for each objective, along with recommended milestones to define the timelines and outcomes. The following section reviews the achievement of key National Emergency Communications Plan initiatives and milestones.

2008 National Emergency Communications Plan Objectives	Key Accomplishments – National Emergency Communications Plan Initiatives and Milestones
Formal Governance Structures and Clear Leadership Roles	• The number of States and territories with full-time Statewide Interoperability Coordinators increased after release of the 2008 National Emergency Communications Plan • DHS published the *Establishing Governance to Achieve Statewide Communications Interoperability: A Guide for Statewide Communication Interoperability Plan Implementation* • More States and territories established Statewide Interoperability Governing Bodies and Statewide Interoperability Executive Committees that incorporated recommended membership criteria • DHS coordinated with SAFECOM to develop the *SAFECOM Recommended Guidance for Federal Grant Programs* (later versions titled *SAFECOM Guidance on Emergency Communications Grants*) annually since Fiscal Year 2009 • The Office of Emergency Communications established the Regional Coordination Program and appointed Regional Coordinators in all 10 Federal Emergency Management Agency (FEMA) Regions • In 2009, the Office of Emergency Communications held a National Conference on Emergency Communications with 475 representatives from the emergency response community and private sector
Coordinated Federal Activities	• The Emergency Communications Preparedness Center formalized its charter and issued its first strategic agenda in 2010

2008 National Emergency Communications Plan Objectives	Key Accomplishments – National Emergency Communications Plan Initiatives and Milestones
	• The Emergency Communications Preparedness Center Grants Focus Group improved coordination of Federal financial assistance programs that fund emergency communications • DHS established the One DHS Emergency Communications Committee to coordinate departmental emergency communications activities • In coordination with other Federal departments and agencies, the Office of Emergency Communications compiled a comprehensive catalog of Federal Technical Assistance programs for emergency communications • DHS and Public Safety Canada established the Canada – United States Communications Interoperability Working Group
Common Planning and Operational Protocols	• The Office of Emergency Communications worked with all States and territories to implement and update their Statewide Communications Interoperability Plan annually • DHS developed the *Plain Language Guide: Making the Transition from Ten Codes to Plain Language* and corresponding guidance for Federal grant programs to further the use of common language • The Office of Emergency Communications developed a reference library of over 200 examples of agreements and standard operating procedures, as well as a suite of templates for emergency communications • DHS worked with more than 150 jurisdictions to develop Tactical Interoperable Communications Pans to document policies associated with establishing interoperable communications within the Urban Areas Security Initiative regions
Standards and Emerging Communications Technologies	• DHS Office for Interoperability and Compatibility established the Project 25 Compliance Assessment Program, a partnership with the National Institute of Standards and Technology, industry representatives, and the emergency response community • Office for Interoperability and Compatibility coordinated with FEMA on standards development and

(Continued)

2008 National Emergency Communications Plan Objectives	Key Accomplishments – National Emergency Communications Plan Initiatives and Milestones
	adoption, conformity assessment, industry capability analysis, stakeholder support, and technology evaluation for the Integrated Public Alert and Warning System • Office for Interoperability and Compatibility published the *Radio over Wireless Broadband Pilot Project Report*, which evaluated a pilot project to test new products and technologies for potential emergency response use • Office for Interoperability and Compatibility published a specifications profile for Voice Over Internet Protocol Bridging System Interface • The Emergency Communications Preparedness Center developed a *Federal Broadband Mission Needs Assessment*, which evaluates Federal broadband communications mission needs and identifies how broadband communications can enhance operational effectiveness • The Office of Emergency Communications completed Technical Assistance broadband workshops in numerous States and territories to help them plan for the Nationwide Public Safety Broadband Network
Emergency Responder Skills and Capabilities	• The Office of Emergency Communications, in partnership with the Office for Interoperability and Compatibility, FEMA, and other stakeholders, developed and implemented a standardized training curriculum for All-Hazards Communication Unit Leaders that complies with the *National Incident Management System*[71] • More than 4,000 emergency responders completed the DHS' All-Hazards Communication Unit Leader course and more than 1,000 have taken the Department's Communications Technician course • The Office of Emergency Communications Technical Assistance Program helped States, territories, local jurisdictions, and tribal nations to design, execute, and evaluate communications exercises • More than 100,000 copies of the *National Interoperability Field Operations Guide* were distributed

2008 National Emergency Communications Plan Objectives	Key Accomplishments – National Emergency Communications Plan Initiatives and Milestones
	to public safety agencies, which provides radio frequency information to assist those establishing or repairing emergency communications in a disaster area
System LifeCycle Planning	• DHS developed a comprehensive *Emergency Communications System Life Cycle Planning Guide* to assist agencies with designing, implementing, supporting, and maintaining public safety communications systems • DHS published the *Interoperability Business Case: An Introduction to Ongoing Local Funding*, a guidance document to help emergency response officials develop compelling business cases to support funding for ongoing local interoperability efforts • The Office of Emergency Communications coordinated with Federal, State, and local stakeholders to collect best practices to develop a lifecycle planning template for grant applicants
Disaster Communications Capabilities	• FEMA published the *State Emergency Communications Planning Methodology and Best Practices*, which provides guidance, best practices, and methodologies for incorporating vulnerability assessments into emergency communications planning, including planning for alternative and backup capabilities when primary systems become unavailable • FEMA developed statewide emergency communications annexes to the Regional Emergency Communications Plans in all 10 FEMA Regions

APPENDIX 7. SOURCE DOCUMENTS AND REFERENCES

This appendix lists the key source documents that the Department of Homeland Security (DHS) used to inform and shape the concepts, goals, and recommendations of the 2014 National Emergency Communications Plan. This list is not exhaustive; rather, it highlights the primary source documents that were developed since the 2008 National Emergency Communications Plan. The references are grouped by author and then in chronological order.

White House	
Cyberspace Policy Review: Assuring a Trusted and Resilient Information and Communications Infrastructure http://www.whitehouse.gov/assets/documents/Cyberspace_Policy_Review_final.pdf	2009
National Security Strategy http://www.whitehouse.gov/sites/default/files/rss_viewer/national_security_strategy.pdf	2010
Digital Government Strategy: Building A 21st Century Platform To Better Serve the American People http://www.whitehouse.gov/sites/default/files/omb/egov/digital-government/digital- government-strategy.pdf	2012
Federal Departments and Agencies	
U.S. Department of Defense (DOD): *Department of Defense Mobile Device Strategy Memorandum* http://www.defense.gov/news/dodmobilitystrategy.pdf	2012
DHS/Federal Emergency Management Agency (FEMA): *National Incident Management System* http://www.fema.gov/pdf/emergency/nims/NIMS_core.pdf	2008
DHS/Office of Emergency Communications: *Establishing Governance to Achieve Statewide Communications Interoperability - A Guide for Statewide Communication Interoperability Plan Implementation* http://www.safecomprogram.gov/oec/establishing_governance_guide.pdf	2008
DHS/FEMA: *The Response to the 2011 Joplin, Missouri Tornado - Lessons Learned Study* https://www.llis.dhs.gov/sites/default/files/Joplin%20Tornado%20Response%20Lessons%20Lear ned%20Report%20Final.pdf	2011
DHS/FEMA: Think Tank Discussion Series on Improving the Emergency Management System http://www.fema.gov/medialibrary/collections/2364	2012
DHS/FEMA: *A Whole Community Approach to Management - Principles, Themes, and Pathways for Action* http://www.fema.gov/media-library-data/20130726-1813-25045-0649/whole_community_dec2011__2_.pdf	2011
DHS/Office of Emergency Communications: *Emergency Communications System Life Cycle Planning Guide* http://www.safecomprogram.gov/oec/oec_system_life_cycle_planning_guide_final.pdf	2011
DHS/Office of Emergency Communications: *National Emergency Communications Plan Urban Area Communications Key Findings and Recommendations* http://www.dhs.gov/national-emergency-communications-plan-	2011

National Emergency Communications Plan -goals	
DHS/Office of Emergency Communications: *Public Safety Communications Evolution Brochure* http://www.safecomprogram.gov/oec/public_safety_communications_ evolution_brochure.pdf	2011
DHS/FEMA: *National Preparedness Report* http://www.fema.gov/national-preparedness-report	2012 2013
DHS/Office of Inspector General: *DHS' Oversight of Interoperable Communications* http://www.oig.dhs.gov/assets/Mgmt/2013/OIG_13-06_Nov12.pdf	2012
DHS/Office of Emergency Communications: *Incident Command System Communications Unit Implementation and Best Practices - A Guide for Program Development* http://www.publicsafetytools.info	2012
DHS/Office of Emergency Communications: *National Summary of Fiscal Year 2011 Statewide Communications Interoperability Plan Implementation Reports* http://www.dhs.gov/statewide- communication-interoperability-plans	2012
DHS/Science and Technology Directorate: *Multi-Band Radio Pilot Report, Operational Assessment* http://www.firstresponder.gov/TechnologyDocuments/Multi%20Band %20Radio%20 Pilot%20Report.pdf	2012
DOD: *Mobile Applications Security Requirements Guide Overview*	2012
U.S. Department of Transportation, National Highway Traffic Safety Administration: National 9-1- 1 Program State of 9-1-1 Webinar Series http://www.9-1-1.gov/webinars.html	2012
FCC: *Recommendations of the Technical Advisory Board for First Responder Interoperability* http://www.fcc.gov/document/recommendations-interoperability-board	2012
FCC: *Uses and Capabilities of Amateur Radio Service Communications in Emergencies and Disaster Relief* http://hraunfoss.fcc.gov/edocs_public/attachmatch/DA-12-1342A1.pdf	2012
DHS/FEMA: *Lessons Learned Report on Boston Marathon Bombings - The Positive Effect of Planning and Preparation on Response* https://www.llis.dhs.gov/sites/default/files/Boston% 20Marathon%20Bombings%20Positive%20Effects%20of%20Prepare dness_0.pdf	2013
DHS/FEMA: *National Response Framework*, Second Edition www.fema.gov/national-response-framework	2013
DHS/Office of Emergency Communications: *Annual SAFECOM*	2013

Guidance on Emergency Communications Grants http://www.safecomprogram.gov/grant.html	
DHS/Office of Emergency Communications: *Emergency Communications Preparedness Center Annual Strategic Assessment - Report to Congress for 2012*	2013
DHS/Office of Emergency Communications: *Emergency Communications Preparedness Center Recommendations to Federal Agencies: Financial Assistance for Emergency Communications* http://www.911.gov/pdf/2011_ECPC_Grants_Recommendations_to_Fed_Agencies_Final.pdf	2013
DHS/Office of Emergency Communications: *National Interoperability Field Operations Guide v1.4* www.publicsafetytools.info/start_nifog_info.php	2013
DHS/Office of Emergency Communications: *Progress Report on Implementing the National Emergency Communications Plan – Fiscal Year 2012 Report to Congress*	2013
DHS/Office of Emergency Communications: *Region IV States and Arkansas & Louisiana Strategic Interstate Communications Resource Allocation Plan*	2013
DHS/Office of Infrastructure Protection: *National Infrastructure Protection Plan* 2013 Version http://www.dhs.gov/national-infrastructure-protection-plan	2013
DHS Science and Technology Directorate: *Lessons Learned: Social Media and Hurricane Sandy Virtual Social Media Working Group and DHS First Responders Group* https://www.llis.dhs.gov/sites/default/files/Lessons%20Learned%20-%20Social%20Media%20and%20Hurricane%20Sandy.pdf	2013
FCC Field Hearing on Superstorm Sandy, New York, NY, and Hoboken, NJ, February 5, 2013 http://www.fcc.gov/events/superstorm-sandy-field-hearing	2013
FCC: *Impact of the June 2012 Derecho on Communications Networks and Services Report and Recommendations* http://www.fcc.gov/document/derecho-report-and-recommendations	2013
FCC: *Legal and Regulatory Framework for Next Generation 911 Services Report to Congress and Recommendations* http://hraunfoss.fcc.gov/edocs_public/attachmatch/DOC-319165A1.pdf	2013
Congressional Panels, Testimonies, And Reports	
Congressional Research Service: *An Emergency Communications Safety Net: Integrating 9-1-1 and Other Services* http://assets.opencrs.com/rpts/RL32939_20080825.pdf	2008
Congressional Research Service: *Social Media and Disasters: Current*	2011

Uses, Future Options, and Policy Considerations http://www.fas.org/sgp/crs/homesec/R41987.pdf	
U.S. Senate Committee on Homeland Security and Governmental Affairs' Subcommittee on Disaster Recovery and Intergovernmental Affairs, Written Statement of Craig Fugate, Administrator, FEMA: *Understanding the Power of Social Media as a Communication Tool in the Aftermath of Disasters*, May 5, 2011 http://www.dhs.gov/news/2011/05/04/written-statement-craig-fugate-administrator-federal- emergency-management-agency	2011
U.S. Senate Committee on Appropriations' Subcommittee on Homeland Security, Written Statement of Craig Fugate, Administrator, FEMA: *Evolution of Emergency Management and Communication*, June 8, 2011 https://www.fema.gov/pdf/about/programs/legislative/testimony/2011/6_8_2011_ evolution_of_emergency_management_and_communication.pdf	2011
Congressional Research Service: *Funding Emergency Communications: Technology and Policy Considerations* http://www.fas.org/sgp/crs/homesec/R41842.pdf	2012
Congressional Research Service: *The First Responder Network and Next-Generation Communications for Public Safety: Issues for Congress* http://www.fas.org/sgp/crs/homesec/R42543.pdf	2013
U.S. House of Representatives Committee on Homeland Security, "The Boston Bombings: A First Look," May 9, 2013 http://homeland.house.gov/hearing/hearing-boston-bombings-first-look	2013
U.S. House of Representatives Committee on Homeland Security Subcommittee on Emergency Preparedness, Response, and Communications Committee, Hearing on "Emergency MGMT 2.0: How Social Media & New Tech Are Transforming Preparedness, Response, & Recovery," June 4 and July 9, 2013 http://homeland.house.gov/hearing/subcommittee-hearing-emergency-mgmt- 20-how-socialmedia-new-tech-are-transforming	2013
U.S. Senate Committee on Homeland Security and Governmental Affairs, Hearing on "Lessons Learned from the Boston Marathon Bombings: Preparing for and Responding to the Attack," July 10, 2013 http://www.hsgac.senate.gov/hearings/lessons-learned-from-the-boston-marathon-bombings- preparing-for-and-responding-to-the-attack	2013
U.S. Senate Committee on Homeland Security and Governmental Affairs, Hearing on "DHS Oversight and Coordination of Research and Development Efforts Could Be Strengthened," Written Statement	2013

of Dave C. Maurer, Director, U.S. Government Accountability Office http://www.gao.gov/assets/660/655898.pdf	
National Associations, Advisory Boards and Groups	
National Governors Association *2009 State Homeland Security Advisors Survey* http://www.nga.org/files/live/sites/NGA/files/pdf/1002HSASURVEY. PDF	2009
Transportation Safety Advancement Group: *Next Generation 9-1-1 What's Next Forum Report and Frequently Asked Questions* http://www.tsag-its.org/docs/2011/08/NG9-1-1%20WN%20FAQ%20-%20August%202011.pdf	2011
National Emergency Management Association Report: *Social Media in the Emergency Management Field - 2012 Survey Results* http://www.cna.org/sites/default/files/research/SocialMedia_Emergenc yManagement.pdf	2013
The National Security Telecommunications Advisory Committee: *Report to the President on the National Security and Emergency Preparedness Implications of a Nationwide Public Safety Broadband Network* https://www.dhs.gov/sites/default/files/publications/npsbn-final-report-05-22- 13_0.pdf	2013

APPENDIX 8. 2008 NATIONAL EMERGENCY COMMUNICATIONS PLAN IMPLEMENTATION CRITERIA

Section 4.0 of the National Emergency Communications Plan outlines the Department of Homeland Security's (DHS) strategy for implementing and measuring the National Emergency Communications Plan in coordination with stakeholders. This includes an assessment of operational communications and a broader evaluation of emergency communications capabilities based on the *SAFECOM Interoperability Continuum* and the capabilities identified in Section 2.3 of the 2008 National Emergency Communications Plan.

This appendix presents the criteria that were used to measure both operational performance and capability levels under the 2008 Plan. To ensure consistency, DHS plans to use the criteria as the foundation to assess nationwide emergency communications. Given changes in the operating environment, DHS will work with the emergency response community to update the criteria as necessary to reflect the use of new technologies and other key developments.

Table A8-1. Operational Performance Criteria

Common Policies and Procedures	
Criteria 1	• Interagency communications policies and procedures were common or consistent amongst all responding agencies
Criteria 2	• Established interagency communications policies and procedures were followed throughout the incident
Criteria 3	• Interagency communications policies and procedures across all responding agencies were consistent with the *National Incident Management System*
Criteria 4	• A priority order for use of interagency communications resources was followed as established in standard operation procedures or plans, such as the Tactical Interoperable Communications Plan
Criteria 5	• A primary interagency operations talk path was clearly established by procedure or communicated to responders early in the incident
Criteria 6	• Common terminology and plain language were used in all interagency communications
Criteria 7	• Clear unit identification procedures were used
Criteria 8	• Common channel names were used for designated interoperability channels
Criteria 9	• Multiple organizations with inherent responsibility for some portion of the incident were present and joined in a unified command with a single individual designated with the Operations Section Chief responsibilities
Criteria 10	• Span of control was maintained amongst the primary operational leadership: the Operations Section Chief and first-level subordinates
Communications System Quality and Continuity	

Criteria 11	• Communications Unit Leader roles and responsibilities were carried out by the Incident Commander/Unified Command or designee. This includes:
	  • Necessary communications resources were effectively ordered using documented procedures; and
	  • A communications plan was established by procedure or developed early in the incident

Criteria 12	• No more than 1 out of 10 transmissions was repeated among the primary operational leadership due to the failure of initial communications attempts
Criteria 13	• Upon failure or overload of any primary communications mode, a backup was provided
Criteria 14	• Primary operational leadership communicated adequately to manage resources and make timely decisions during the incident or event

Table A8-2. Capability Criteria

Capability	Early Implementation	Intermediate Implementation	Established Implementation	Advanced Implementation
Governance	Area decision-making groups are informal and do not yet have a strategic plan to guide collective communications interoperability goals and funding	Some formal agreements exist and informal agreements are in practice among members of the decision-making group for the area; strategic and budget planning processes are beginning to be put in place	Formal agreements outline the roles and responsibilities of an area-wide decision-making group, which has an agreed upon strategic plan that addresses sustainable funding for collective, regional interoperable communications needs	Area-wide decision-making bodies proactively look to expand membership to ensure repres-entation from broad public support disciplines and other levels of government, while updating their agreements and strategic plan on a regular basis
Standard Operating Procedures – Policies, Practices, and Procedures	Area-wide interoperable communications standard operating procedures are not developed or have not been formalized and disseminated	Some interoperable communications standard operating procedures exist within the area and steps have been taken to institute these interoperability procedures among some agencies	Interoperable communications standard operating procedures are formalized and in use by all agencies within the area. Despite minor issues, standard operating procedures are successfully used during responses and/or exercises	Interoperable communications standard operating procedures within the area are formalized and regularly reviewed. Additionally, the *National Incident Management System* procedures are well established among all agencies and disciplines. All needed procedur-es are effectively utilized during responses and/or exercises
Training and Exercise – Emergency Responder Skills and Capabilities	Area-wide public safety agencies participate in communications interoperability workshops, but no formal training or exercises are focused on emergency communications	Some public safety agencies within the area hold communications interoperability training on equipment and conduct exercises, although not on a regular cycle	Public safety agencies within the area participate in equipment and Standard Operating Procedure training for communications interoperability and hold exercises on a regular schedule	Area public safety agencies regularly conduct training and exercises with communications interoperability curriculum addressing equipment and standard operating procedures that is modified as needed to address

Capability	Early Implementation	Intermediate Implementation	Established Implementation	Advanced Implementation
				the changing operational environment
Usage	First responders across the area seldom use solutions unless advanced planning is possible (e.g., special events)	First responders across the area use interoperability solutions regularly for emergency events, and in limited fashion for day-to-day communications	First responders across the area use interoperability solutions regularly and easily for all day-to-day, task force, and mutual aid events	Regular use of solutions for all day-to-day and out-of-the-ordinary events across the area on demand, in real time, when needed, as authorized
Technology	Interoperability within the area is primarily achieved through the use of gateways (mobile/fixed gateway, console patch), shared radios, or use of a radio cache	Interoperability within the area is primarily achieved through the use of shared channels or talk groups	Interoperability within the area is primarily achieved through the use of a proprietary shared system	Interoperability within the area is primarily achieved through the use of standards-based shared system (e.g., Project 25)

APPENDIX 9. GLOSSARY

After-Action Report. A professional document formulated in partnership with participants in a process. Evaluators, sponsoring agencies, and key participants from government agencies participate in the formulation of the after-action report. It furnishes a historical record of findings and forms the foundation for refinements to plans, policies, procedures, training, equipment, and overall preparedness of an entity. The report depicts the process, preliminary observations, and major issues, and makes recommendations for improvements.

Applications. A set of features and a user interface that may be realized by fixed or mobile devices. User services are logical building blocks of application-layer functionality.

Agreements. Formal mechanisms to govern interagency coordination and the use of interoperable emergency communications solutions.

Assessment. The process of acquiring, collecting, processing, examining, analyzing, evaluating, monitoring, and interpreting the data, information, evidence, objects, measurements, images, and sound, among others, whether tangible or intangible, to provide a basis for decision-making.

Amateur Radio Service. A radio communication service for the purpose of self-training, intercommunication, and technical investigations carried out by amateurs, who are duly authorized persons interested in radio technique solely with a personal aim and without pecuniary interest.

Auxiliary Communications. Backup emergency radio communications provided by volunteers who support public safety and emergency response professionals and their agencies.

Broadband. High-speed Internet that allows users to access the Internet and Internet-related services at significantly higher speeds than those available through dial-up Internet access services. Broadband allows users to access information via the Internet using one of several high-speed transmission technologies: Digital Subscriber Line; Cable Modem; Fiber; Wireless; and Satellite. Transmission is digital, meaning that text, images, and sound are all transmitted as bits of data. The transmission technologies that make broadband possible move these bits much more quickly than traditional telephone or wireless connections.

Common Alerting Protocol. The Common Alerting Protocol is a digital format for exchanging emergency alerts that allows a consistent alert message to be disseminated simultaneously over many different communications systems.

Communications Unit. Within the Incident Command System, an organizational unit in the Logistics Section that is responsible for effective incident communications planning, especially in the context of a multi-agency incident. Additionally, this unit installs and tests all communications equipment, supervises and operates the incident communications center, distributes and recovers communications equipment assigned to incident personnel, and maintains and repairs communications equipment on site.

Continuity of Communications. The ability of emergency response agencies to maintain communications capabilities when primary infrastructure is damaged or destroyed.

Core Capabilities. Distinct critical elements necessary to achieve the *National Preparedness Goal.*

Critical Infrastructure. Systems and assets, whether physical or virtual, so vital to the United States that the incapacity or destruction of such systems and assets would have a debilitating impact on security, national economic security, national public health or medical, or safety, or any combination of those matters. (Source: *2013 National Infrastructure Protection Plan*)

Cross-Discipline. Involving emergency response providers from different disciplines (e.g., police, fire, emergency medical services).

Cybersecurity. The prevention of damage to, unauthorized use of, or exploitation of, and, if needed, the restoration of electronic information and communications systems and the information contained therein to ensure confidentiality, integrity, and availability. Includes protection and restoration, when needed, of information networks and wireline, wireless, satellite, public safety answering points, and 9-1-1 communications systems and control systems. (Source: *2013 National Infrastructure Protection Plan 2013: Partnering for Critical Infrastructure Security and Resilience*)

Dispatch Center. Agency or interagency dispatch centers, 9-1-1 call centers (e.g., public safety answering points), emergency control or command dispatch centers, or any naming convention given to the facility and staff that handles emergency calls from the public and communication with emergency management/response personnel.

Emergency Communications. The means and methods for exchanging communications and information necessary for successful incident management.

Emergency Management Assistance Compact. A congressionally ratified mutual aid compact that legally establishes a national system to facilitate resources across State lines during an emergency or disaster.

Emergency Response Providers. *The Homeland Security Act of 2002* defines emergency response providers as Federal, State, and local governmental and nongovernmental emergency public safety, fire, law enforcement, emergency response, emergency medical (including hospital emergency facilities), and related personnel, agencies, and authorities.

Emergency Support Functions. Used by the Federal Government and many State governments as the primary mechanism at the operational level to organize and provide assistance. Emergency Support Functions align categories of resources and provide strategic objectives for their use. Emergency Support Functions utilize standardized resource management concepts such as typing, inventorying, and tracking to facilitate the dispatch, deployment, and recovery of resources before, during, and after an incident.

Exercises. Instruments to train for, assess, practice, and improve performance in prevention, protection, mitigation, response, and recovery capabilities in a risk-free environment. Exercises can be used for testing and validating policies, plans, procedures, training, equipment, and interagency agreements; clarifying and training personnel in roles and responsibilities; improving interagency coordination and communications; improving individual performance; identifying gaps in resources; and identifying opportunities for improvement.

First Responder Network Authority. An independent authority within the National Telecommunications and Information Administration that is responsible for ensuring the building, deployment, and operation of the first high-speed, nationwide public safety broadband network.

First Responders. See "emergency response provider." (The *Implementing the 9/11 Commission Recommendations Act of 2007* states that the term first responder shall have the same meaning as the term emergency response provider, which is defined in the *Homeland Security Act of 2002*.)

Government Emergency Telecommunications Service. Service that provides national security and emergency preparedness personnel priority access and prioritized processing in the local and long distance segments of the Public Switched Telephone Network, greatly increasing the probability of call completion. Government Emergency Telecommunications Service is intended to be used in an emergency or crisis situation when the Public Switched Telephone Network is congested and the probability of completing a normal call is reduced.

Governance. Relates to consistent management, cohesive policies, guidance, processes, and decision-rights for a given area of responsibility.

Incident Action Plan. An oral or written plan containing general objectives reflecting the overall strategy for managing an incident. It may include the identification of operational resources and assignments. It may also include attachments that provide direction and important information for management of the incident during one or more operational periods.

Incident Command System. A standardized on-scene emergency management construct specifically designed to provide for the adoption of an integrated organizational structure that reflects the complexity and demands of single or multiple incidents, without being hindered by jurisdictional boundaries. The incident command system is the combination of facilities, equipment, personnel, procedures, and communications operating within a common organizational structure, designed to aid in the management of resources during incidents. It is used for all kinds of emergencies and is applicable to small and large, complex incidents. The incident command system is used by various jurisdictions and functional agencies, both public and private, to organize field-level incident management operations.

Information Sharing Environment. Broadly refers to the people, projects, systems, and agencies that enable responsible information sharing for national security.

Internet Protocol-Based Technologies. Any component, device, application, or system designed to function on an Internet Protocol network.

Interoperability. Ability of emergency responders to communicate among jurisdictions, disciplines, frequency bands, and levels of government as needed and as authorized. System operability is required for system interoperability.

Jurisdiction. A range or sphere of authority. Public safety agencies have jurisdiction at an incident related to their legal responsibilities and authority. Jurisdictional authority at an incident can be political or geographical (e.g., Federal, State, tribal, local boundary lines) or functional (e.g., law enforcement, public health, medical).

Land Mobile Radio Systems. Terrestrially-based wireless narrowband communications systems commonly used by Federal, State, local, tribal, and territorial emergency responders, public works companies, and even the military to support voice and low-speed data communications.

Lifecycle Planning. The process of designing, implementing, supporting, and maintaining a land mobile radio or mobile data-based public safety communications system. Enables practitioners to better forecast long-term funding requirements and helps to set the framework for establishing and maintaining a public safety system.

Long-Term Evolution. The next evolution of commercial broadband wireless communications technology, which was developed to address the demand for high-speed, data intensive communications, such as situational awareness, advanced analytics, database queries, and video applications.

Mission Areas. Groups of core capabilities, including Prevention, Protection, Mitigation, Response, and Recovery. (Source: *National Preparedness Goal*)

Multi-jurisdictional. Involving agencies from different jurisdictions (e.g., across State, county, or regional boundaries).

Mutual Aid Agreement or Assistance Agreement: Written or oral agreement between and among agencies, organizations, or jurisdictions that provides a mechanism to quickly obtain emergency assistance in the form of personnel, equipment, materials, and other associated services. The primary objective is to facilitate rapid, short-term deployment of emergency support prior to, during, or after an incident.

National Emergency Communications Plan. The *Homeland Security Act of 2002*, as amended, requires DHS to develop the National Emergency Communications Plan; the Plan serves as the Nation's strategic plan for improving emergency response communications and efforts in the United States.

National Incident Management System. Provides a systematic, proactive approach and template to guide departments and agencies at all levels of government, nongovernmental organizations, and the private sector to work seamlessly to prevent, protect against, respond to, recover from, and mitigate the effects of incidents, regardless of cause, size, location, or complexity, in order to reduce the loss of life or property and harm to the environment.

National Preparedness Goal. The cornerstone for the implementation of Presidential Policy Directive-8, it establishes the capabilities and outcomes for the Nation to accomplish across five mission areas (Prevention, Protection, Mitigation, Response, and Recovery) in order to be secure and resilient. The Goal establishes distinct core capabilities and corresponding target elements for each mission area.

Nationwide Public Safety Broadband Network. A dedicated, wireless, interoperable, communications long-term evolution-based network (consisting of a core network and radio access network) that allows public safety to receive and share critical information with their counterparts across the Nation.

National Response Framework. A guide to how the Nation responds to all types of disasters and emergencies. It describes specific authorities and best practices for managing incidents that range from the serious but purely local to large-scale terrorist attacks or catastrophic natural disasters.

National Security and Emergency Preparedness Communications Functions. The ability of the Federal Government to communicate at all times and under all circumstances to carry out its most critical and time sensitive missions. This includes the survivable, resilient, enduring, and effective communications, both domestic and international, that are essential to enable the executive branch to communicate within itself and with: the legislative and judicial branches; State, local, tribal, and territorial governments; private sector entities; and the public, allies, and other nations.

Nongovernmental Organization. As noted in the *National Response Framework*, these include voluntary, racial and ethnic, faith-based, veteran-based, and nonprofit organizations that provide sheltering, emergency food supplies, and other essential support services. Nongovernmental organizations are inherently independent and committed to specific interests and values.

Operability. Ability of emergency responders to establish and sustain communications in support of mission operations.

Operating Environment. For the purposes of the National Emergency Communications Plan, this refers to the people, processes, policies, and technologies for emergency communications.

Private Sector Entity. Per the *National Response Framework*, private sector entities include large, medium, and small businesses; commerce, private cultural and educational institutions; and industry, as well as public-private partnerships that have been established specifically for emergency management purposes.

Public Safety Entity. An entity that provides public safety services and that include services provided by emergency response providers, as defined in the *Homeland Security Act of 2002* (see above definition for "emergency response providers"). (Source: *Middle Class Tax Relief and Job Creation Act of 2012*)

Public Safety Services. Includes services defined in the *Communications Act of 1934* as those with the sole or principal purpose of which is to protect the safety of life, health, or property; that are provided—by State or local government entities; or by nongovernmental organizations that are authorized by a governmental entity whose primary mission is the provision of such services; and that are not made commercially available to the public by the provider. Also includes services provided by emergency response providers, as defined in Section 2 of the *Homeland Security Act of 2002* (see above definition for "emergency response providers").

Public Safety Answering Point. A facility that has been designated to receive 9-1-1 calls and route them to emergency services personnel. A Public Safety Answering Point may act as a dispatch center. Public Safety Answering Point is often used with the term Public Safety Communications Center. (Source: *Communications Act of 1934*, as amended)

Reliability. Achieved in public safety land mobile radio systems through equipment redundancy and minimizing single points of failures through careful system design. System operators stock spare parts and, in some cases, transportable backup systems to restore system failures that do occur. Reliability must be considered at the earliest stages of system design.

Redundancy. Additional or alternate systems, sub-systems, assets, or processes that maintain a degree of overall functionality in case of loss or failure of another system, sub-system, asset, or process.

Resources. Personnel and major items of equipment, supplies, and facilities available or potentially available for assignment to incident operations and for which status is maintained. Resources are described by kind and type and may be used in operational support or supervisory capacities at an incident or at an Emergency Operations Center.

Response-Level Emergency Communications. Per the 2008 National Emergency Communications Plan, response-level emergency communications are the capacity of individuals with primary operational leadership responsibility to manage resources and make timely decisions during a multi-agency incident without technical or procedural communications impediments. In addition to communicating to first-level subordinates in the field, the Operations Section Chief should be able to communicate upwards to the incident command level (e.g., between the Operations Section Chief and Incident Command).

Social Media. Refers to the means of interactions among people in which they create, share, or exchange information and ideas in virtual communities and networks.

Standard Operating Procedures. Generally refers to a reference document or an operations manual that provides the purpose, authorities, duration, and details for the preferred method of performing a single function or a number of interrelated functions in a uniform manner.

Strategic Planning. Planning process that establishes organizational goals and identifies, scopes, and establishes requirements for the provisioning of capabilities and resources to achieve them.

Statewide Communication Interoperability Plan. Stakeholder-driven, multi-jurisdictional, and multi-disciplinary statewide plans that outline and define the current and future vision for communications interoperability within the State or territory. The Statewide Communications Interoperability Plan is a critical strategic planning tool to help States prioritize resources, establish and strengthen governance, identify future technology investments, and address interoperability gaps.

Statewide Interoperability Coordinator. Serves as the State's single point of contact for interoperable communications and implements the Statewide Communication Interoperability Plan.

Statewide Interoperability Governing Bodies. Serves as the primary steering group for the statewide interoperability strategy. Its mission is to support the National Council of Statewide Interoperability Coordinators in efforts to improve emergency response communications across the State through enhanced data and voice communications interoperability. They often include representatives from various jurisdictions, disciplines, as well as subject matter experts.

Statewide Interoperability Executive Committees. Used interchangeably with Statewide Interoperability Governing Bodies.

Tactical Interoperable Communications Plan. A plan providing rapid provision of on-scene, incident based mission critical voice communications among all first responder agencies (e.g., emergency medical services, fire, and law enforcement), as appropriate for the incident, and in support of an incident command system as defined in the *National Incident Management System.*

Technical Assistance. Support to State, local, tribal, and territorial emergency responders and government officials through the development and delivery of training, tools, and onsite assistance to advance public safety interoperable communications capabilities.

Technology. Per the *SAFECOM Interoperability Continuum*, applies to a capability element that encompasses the systems and equipment that enable emergency responders to share information efficiently and securely during an emergency incident, and addresses the functionality, performance, interoperability, and continuity capabilities of those systems and equipment.

Telecommunications Service Priority. A program that authorizes organizations to receive priority treatment for vital voice and data circuits or other telecommunications services. The Telecommunications Service Priority program provides service vendors a Federal Communications Commission mandate to prioritize requests by identifying those services critical to national security and emergency preparedness. A telecommunications service priority assignment ensures that it will receive priority attention by the service vendor before any non-telecommunications service priority service.

Usage. Per the *SAFECOM Interoperability Continuum*, this applies to the frequency and familiarity with which emergency responders use interoperable emergency communications solutions.

Wireless Priority Service. Service offering that provides national security and emergency preparedness personnel with priority access and prioritized processing in all nationwide and several regional cellular networks, greatly increasing the probability of call completion. It is intended to be used in an emergency or crisis situation when cellular networks are congested and the probability of completing a normal cellular call is reduced.

Whole Community. Per the *National Preparedness Goal*, the term whole community applies to the focus on enabling the participation in national preparedness activities of a wider range of players from the private and nonprofit sectors, including nongovernmental organizations and the general public, in conjunction with the participation of Federal, State, local, tribal, and territorial governmental partners in order to foster better coordination and working relationships.

APPENDIX 10. ACRONYMS

DHS	Department of Homeland Security
FCC	Federal Communications Commission
FEMA	Federal Emergency Management Agency

End Notes

[1] Title 6 United States Code, § 572.

[2] See Appendix 5 for more information on the *SAFECOM Interoperability Continuum*.

[3] The term "response" is defined in the *National Preparedness Goal* and *National Response Framework*. The Goal establishes the capabilities and outcomes the Nation must accomplish in order to be secure and resilient. The *National Response Framework* is a guide to how the Nation responds to all types of disasters and emergencies. http://www.fema.gov/national-response-framework.

[4] Federal Emergency Management Agency. *A Whole Community Approach to Emergency Management: Principles, Themes,and Pathways for Action*, December 2011, pg. 2.

[5] Title XVIII of the *Homeland Security Act of 2002* (Public Law 109-295).

[6] Appendix 1 provides a legislative compliance matrix that maps the National Emergency Communications Plan to its requirements in Title 6 United States Code § 572.

[7] Executive Order 13618, *Assignment of National Security and Emergency Preparedness Communications Functions,* assigns national security and emergency preparedness communications functions to Federal Government entities to ensure Executive Branch communications at all times and under all circumstances to carry out its most critical and time sensitive missions.

[8] The *National Response Framework* defines private sector entities as large, medium, and small businesses; commerce, private cultural and educational institutions; and industry, as well as public-private partnerships that have been established specifically for emergency management purposes.

[9] Current and future versions of the *Quadrennial Homeland Security Review* can be found at http://www.dhs.gov/quadrennial- homeland-security-review-qhsr.

[10] For purposes of the National Emergency Communications Plan, the terms "share information" or "information sharing" refer to the exchange of data, information, or knowledge between various organizations, people, and technologies.

[11] Per the *National Response Framework*, nongovernmental organizations include voluntary, racial and ethnic, faith-based, veteran-based, and nonprofit organizations that provide sheltering, emergency food supplies, and other essential support services. Nongovernmental organizations are inherently independent and committed to specific interests and values.

[12] 6 United States Code § 572.

[13] See Appendix 6 for a summary of progress implementing the 2008 National Emergency Communications Plan.

[14] Per the *National Preparedness Goal*, whole community is formally defined as, "A focus on enabling the participation in national preparedness activities of a wider range of players

from the private and nonprofit sectors, including nongovernmental organizations and the general public, in conjunction with the participation of Federal, State, and local governmental partners in order to foster better coordination and working relationships." Refer to Appendix 4, *Roles and Responsibilities*, for more information on the whole community.

[15] Applying Fair Information Practice Principles to government and private sector stakeholder programs is a best practice for ensuring that privacy protections are included. The Fair Information Practice Principles are the widely-accepted framework of principles used to assess and mitigate privacy impacts of information systems, processes, or programs. It contains eight interdependent principles: Transparency, Individual Participation, Purpose Specification, Data Minimization, Use Limitation, Data Quality and Integrity, Security, and Accountability and Auditing. These principles form a framework that can be applied to any type of information collection, use, or sharing activity; the exact implementation of each principle, however, will vary based upon context.

[16] The 2013 *National Infrastructure Protection Plan* defines cybersecurity as "the prevention of damage to, unauthorized use of, or exploitation of, and, if needed, the restoration of electronic information and communications systems and the information contained therein to ensure confidentiality, integrity, and availability. Includes protection and restoration, when needed, of information networks and wireline, wireless, satellite, public safety answering points, and 9-1-1 communications systems and control systems." http://www.dhs.gov/national-infrastructure-protection-plan.

[17] In February 2014, the National Institute of Standards and Technology released Version 1.0 of the *Framework for Improving Critical Infrastructure Cybersecurity*. The document, created through collaboration between the government and the private sector, is a voluntary risk-based approach to cybersecurity that uses industry guidelines to help organizations manage cyber risks to critical infrastructure. http://www.nist.gov/cyberframework/upload/cybersecurity-framework-021214-final.pdf.

[18] This graphic depicts the key uses and functions of emergency communications during emergencies. It should not be viewed as linear, as emergency communications are increasingly dynamic and multi-directional. For example, although communications in many emergency situations start with an individual's request for assistance, emergencies may start with a Federal, State, local, tribal, or territorial government agency's communications warning of an impending threat or weather situation.

[19] FCC Disaster Information Reporting System: http://transition.fcc.gov/pshs/services/cip/dirs/dirs.html.

[20] FCC Network Outage Reporting System: http://transition.fcc.gov/pshs/services/cip/nors/nors.html.

[21] This is a notional scenario. While each of the applications is feasible today, it is not anticipated that all jurisdictions or communities will be required or able to implement these capabilities.

[22] The National Emergency Communications Plan goals and objectives align to the elements of the *SAFECOM Interoperability Continuum*. DHS developed the *SAFECOM Interoperability Continuum* in partnership with the public safety community to help agencies and jurisdictions identify their communications needs and track progress in implementing them. See Appendix 5 for more information.

[23] 6 United States Code § 572. Refer to Appendix 1 for a crosswalk of the legislative requirements to sections of the Plan.

[24] Prior to the establishment of the Office of Emergency Communication, only eight States had developed strategic plans for emergency communications. Currently, all 56 States and territories have Statewide Communication Interoperability Plans and work with the Office of Emergency Communications to update them on an annual basis to improve interoperability statewide.

[25] The *Fiscal Year 2007 Department of Homeland Security Appropriations Act* (Public Law 109-295) established the Emergency Communications Preparedness Center to improve

coordination of Federal emergency communications efforts, including information sharing, planning, operations, grants, and technical assistance. The Act also directs the Emergency Communications Preparedness Center to coordinate Federal aspects of the National Emergency Communications Plan.

[26] The *Middle Class Tax Relief and Job Creation Act of 2012* (Public Law 112-96) created the First Responder Network Authority, as an independent authority within the National Telecommunications and Information Administration, to provide emergency responders with the first high-speed, nationwide network dedicated to public safety.

[27] Established in 2005, the All Hazards Consortium is focused on homeland security and emergency management issues and involves representatives from the States of North Carolina, Maryland, Virginia, West Virginia, Delaware, Pennsylvania, New Jersey, and New York, as well as New York City-NY, Newark-NJ, Philadelphia-PA, and the National Capital Region (Washington D.C.).

[28] In a December 7, 2012, memo from the First Responder Network Authority Board Chairman to the Under Secretary for National Protection & Programs Directorate, the First Responder Network Authority expressed its plan to utilize the Emergency Communications Preparedness Center as an ongoing means of interacting and collaborating with key Federal stakeholder agencies on network deployment and operations matters.

[29] Executive Order 13618, *Assignment of National Security and Emergency Preparedness Communications Functions*, July 2012.

[30] The *SAFECOM Guidance on Emergency Communications Grants* provides grantees with information on emergency communications policies and technical standards for improving interoperability. The SAFECOM Guidance is updated annually and can be found at www.safecomprogram.gov.

[31] The *2013 Emergency Communications Preparedness Center Recommendations to Federal Agencies: Financial Assistance for Emergency Communications* sets the national strategy for Federal financial assistance programs that fund emergency communications—including grants, loans, and cooperative agreements.

[32] DHS, Critical Infrastructure Sector Partnerships Home Page. http://www.dhs.gov/critical-infrastructure-sector-partnerships.

[33] The Common Alerting Protocol is a digital format for exchanging emergency alerts that allows a consistent alert message to be disseminated simultaneously over many different communications systems. http://www.fema.gov/common-alerting-protocol.

[34] The Information Sharing Environment broadly refers to the people, projects, systems, and agencies that enable responsible information sharing for national security. https://www.ise.gov.

[35] The National Public Safety Telecommunications Council Broadband Working Group and its task groups research and define public safety broadband requirements in a number of key areas. http://www.npstc.org/broadband.jsp.

[36] As discussed in Goal 4, the DHS Communications Asset Survey and Mapping Tool provides a capability to document each State and territories' fixed and transportable assets.

[37] The Office of Emergency Communications Technical Assistance Program provides a variety of tools to assist States and territories with planning for Nationwide Public Safety Broadband Network deployment in coordination with the First Responder Network Authority. See http://www.publicsafetytools.info for more information.

[38] DHS components should use the One DHS process to ensure a coordinated approach for departmental activities.

[39] More information on Wireless Priority Service, Telecommunications Service Priority, and Government Emergency Telecommunications Service can be found at http://www.dhs.gov/about-office-emergency-communications under "Related Resources" on the right.

[40] Homeland Security Exercise and Evaluation Program policy and guidance is available at https://www.llis.dhs.gov/hseep.

[41] National Level Exercise 2011 was a Tier 1 exercise that occurred on May 16-19, 2011. Tier 1 exercises are mandated by Congress and coordinated by FEMA. The functional exercise component of National Level Exercise 2011 began with a simulated earthquake along the New Madrid fault line. It included more than 10,000 Federal, State, regional, local, private sector, and nongovernmental organization participants.

[42] More information on Communication Unit Leader and Communications Technician courses can be found at http://www.dhs.gov/video/communications-unit-leader-training#.

[43] DHS, *Progress Report on Implementing the National Emergency Communications Plan: Fiscal Year 2012 Report to Congress*, April 17, 2013, pg. 16.

[44] The Communications Unit is led by a Communication Unit Leader and includes Communication Technicians, incident communications center personnel, and technical specialists, all of whom can provide expertise and resources to maintain effective communications throughout an incident or event.

[45] Interoperability channels are radio channels used for multi-disciplinary and multi-jurisdictional response. Planning radio channel usage and programming interoperability channels into radios in advance of emergencies or planned events can enhance preparedness and communications.

[46] *National Interoperability Field Operations Guide Sixth Printing*, April 2013. http://www.publicsafetytools.info/start_nifog_info.php.

[47] DHS, Office of Emergency Communications Public Safety Technical Assistance Tools Home Page. http://www.publicsafetytools.info.

[48] FCC. *Impact of the June 2012 Derecho on Communications Networks and Services*, January 2013, http://www.fcc.gov/document/derecho-report-and-recommendations.

[49] The National Emergency Number Association provides Public Safety Answering Points with resources for Continuity of Operations and disaster planning. http://www.nena.org/?page=COP_PlanCourse.

[50] Established in 2006, the National Joint Telecommunicator Emergency Response Task Force Initiative is a partnership between the National Emergency Number Association and the Association of Public-Safety Communications Officials —International.

[51] Department of Commerce, Public Safety Communications Research Program Overview Home Page. http://www.pscr.gov.

[52] Department of Defense. *Mobile Device Strategy.* http://www.defense.gov/news/dodmobilitystrategy.pdf.

[53] The *Middle Class Tax Relief and Job Creation Act of 2012* (Public Law 112-96) required the First Responder Network Authority to establish a standing public safety advisory committee to assist them in carrying out its duties and responsibilities. http://www.ntia.doc.gov/files/ntia/publications/firstnet_psac_org_chart_and_membership-022013.pdf.

[54] Project 25 resulted in the Telecommunications Industry Association 102 suite of standards for public safety Land Mobile Radio and will need to be supported during the development of transitional solutions that permit and maintain interoperability between legacy Land Mobile Radio communications and long-term evolution networks.

[55] For more information on the Project 25 Compliance Assessment Program, see: http://www.pscr.gov/ outreach/safecom/p25_cap/p25_cap_docs.php.

[56] This methodology aligns with the *National Preparedness System's* six components that provide a consistent and reliable approach to support decision-making, resource allocation, and measuring progress toward building, maintaining, and sustaining capabilities.

[57] Appendix 4 addresses the key stakeholders responsible for executing the National Emergency Communications Plan's recommended strategies.

[58] The criteria used to measure operational performance and interoperability capabilities are presented in Appendix 8.

[59] The Office of Emergency Communications developed the *Communications Interoperability Performance Measurement Guide* to assist public safety officials with measuring the National Emergency Communications Plan goals and assessing performance of

interoperable communications on a regular basis. http://www.safecomprogram.gov/oec/oec_performance_measurement_guide.pdf.

[60] Title XVIII of the *Homeland Security Act of 2002* requires the Office of Emergency Communications to report to Congress on DHS' progress toward achieving national emergency communications goals. In addition, the law requires the Emergency Communications Preparedness Center to report to Congress annually on Federal agencies' progress.

[61] Title XVIII of the *Homeland Security Act of 2002*

[62] DHS, *Quadrennial Homeland Security Review*, June 2014. http://www.dhs.gov/quadrennial-homeland-security-review-qhsr.

[63] White House. Presidential Policy Directive – 8, *National Preparedness*, March 2011. http://www.fema.gov/ppd8.

[64] Federal Emergency Management Agency. *2013 National Preparedness Report to Congress*. May 2013.

[65] Each State has the ability to designate other officials and offices to oversee aspects of emergency communications and information technology.

[66] For a list of all core capabilities, refer to the *National Preparedness Goal*, www.fema.gov/ppd8.

[67] FEMA. *National Response Framework*, June 2013, pg. 8. http://www.fema.gov/national-response-framework.

[68] As defined by the 2008 National Emergency Communications Plan, response-level communications is the capacity of individuals with primary operational leadership responsibility to manage resources and make timely decisions during an incident.

[69] The National Emergency Communications Plan Goal 1 National Report is available at: http://www.dhs.gov/xlibrary/assets/necp_goal_1_findings_accessible.pdf.

[70] For more information on the *SAFECOM Interoperability Continuum*, refer to Appendix 5.

[71] Refer to the *Incident Command System Communications Unit Implementation and Best Practices - A Guide for Program Development*. See http://www.publicsafetytools.info for more information.

In: National Emergency Communications Plan   ISBN: 978-1-63463-899-9
Editor: Carl R. Bush   © 2015 Nova Science Publishers, Inc.

Chapter 2

THE FIRST RESPONDER NETWORK (FIRSTNET) AND NEXT-GENERATION COMMUNICATIONS FOR PUBLIC SAFETY: ISSUES FOR CONGRESS[*]

Linda K. Moore

SUMMARY

Since September 11, 2001, when communications failures contributed to the tragedies of the day, Congress has passed several laws intended to create a nationwide emergency communications capability. Yet the United States has continued to strive for a solution that assures seamless communications among first responders and emergency personnel at the scene of a major disaster. To address this problem, Congress included provisions in the Middle Class Tax Relief and Job Creation Act of 2012 (P.L. 112-96) for planning, building, and managing a new, nationwide, broadband network for public safety communications (FirstNet), and assigned additional radio frequency spectrum to accommodate the new network. In addition, the act has designated federal appropriations of over $7 billion for the network and other public safety needs. These funds will be provided through new revenue from the auction of spectrum licenses. These and other public safety and spectrum

---

[*] This is an edited, reformatted and augmented version of a Congressional Research Service publication R42543, prepared for Members and Committees of Congress, dated March 12, 2014.

provisions of the act appear in Title VI, known as the Public Safety and Spectrum Act, or Spectrum Act.

There are many challenges for public safety leaders and policy makers in establishing the framework for a nationwide network that meets state, local, and tribal needs for robust, interoperable emergency communications. For example, emergency communications networks currently operate on separate networks using different technologies. Because public safety planning has lagged behind commercial efforts to build next-generation wireless networks, the work on design and development of technical requirements for a public safety broadband network is incomplete. Furthermore, each state has its own laws and procedures for building, managing, and funding its network. Establishing a governance model that accommodates current investments and future needs without compromising the coherence of a national network is another challenge. The cost of construction of a nationwide network for public safety is estimated by experts to be in the tens of billions of dollars over the long term, with similarly large sums needed for maintenance and operation. In expectation that private sector participation in building the new network will reduce costs to the public sector, the law has provided some requirements and guidelines for partnerships, access to spectrum, and shared use of infrastructure. Identifying and negotiating with potential partners is another challenge for the new network, as is establishing a revenue stream to fund operations and future investments. These and other challenges are potential barriers to the success of the new network. To meet them in a timely manner may require significant investments in human resources in the early stages of the network. Therefore, yet another challenge to success may arise from federal hiring requirements and the release of funds to cover salaries and expenses while FirstNet is in start-up mode.

In addition to monitoring progress in building the new broadband network for public safety, Congress may want to consider reviewing the role of commercial networks in emergency response and recovery. Once commercial communications lines are compromised because of infrastructure failures, interdependent public safety networks are threatened and the ability to communicate vital information to the public is diminished. New policy initiatives may be needed to identify critical gaps in communications infrastructure and the means to fund the investments needed to close these gaps.

INTRODUCTION

The importance of wireless communications in emergency response has expanded in parallel with increasing reliance on mobile communications across all sectors of the American economy. The consequences of failure in emergency communications networks have also grown, as the nation witnessed on September 11, 2001, and in the days that followed, as first responders and other emergency workers struggled to communicate with each other. The need for robust emergency communications was again underlined by network failures in the wakes of Hurricanes Katrina and Rita, in 2005. Fixing the problems of communications interoperability and operability that hampered response and recovery in these and other catastrophic events has been and remains a long-term goal of policy makers.

After September 11, many experts recognized that a first responder communications network with national coverage would provide the standards and connectivity needed for interoperability and survivability. The National Commission on Terrorist Attacks Upon the United States (9/11 Commission) also recognized the role of networks in providing interoperability, citing the Army Signal Corps as a possible model in recommendations to Congress.[1]

From 2002 through 2007 Congress passed several laws intended to provide the Department of Homeland Security with the tools to plan for a national network. Efforts fell short of congressional expectations, however, in part because federal resources were directed to maintaining local jurisdiction in decision-making at the expense of coordinating a nationwide network.[2]

With the passage of the "Spectrum Act," Title VI of the Middle Class Tax Relief and Job Creation Act of 2012 (P.L. 112-96) on February 22, 2012, the Administration, Congress, the public safety sector, and many other stakeholders have come together to begin the process of developing, constructing, and operating a nationwide network designed to meet public safety communications needs. The act has given government agencies and public safety officials new tools for providing nationwide availability of state-of-the art communications capability for emergency response and recovery. A new network is to be built to provide broadband communications "on a single, national network architecture that evolves with technological advancements."[3] The act requires that recommended minimum technology standards be based on commercial Long Term Evolution (LTE).[4] LTE is a fourth-generation wireless technology that bases its operating standards on the Internet Protocol (IP). IP-enabled networks and wireless devices provide higher capacity and transmission speeds than earlier generations of technology. It is generally believed that the use of LTE and IP standards will greatly enhance communications for emergency response and recovery.

The initial network features specified in the act are consistent with LTE network architectures but might be applied to other technologies introduced for wireless communications. One of the limitations of LTE standards is that they are based on earlier cellular networks and do not take full advantage of the Internet.[5] Therefore, although compatibility with current and evolving commercial LTE technology is deemed by most to be essential for the early stages of its development, FirstNet is not limited to LTE or LTE Advanced. The emphasis in the Spectrum Act appears to be on tapping the innovative energy of the commercial sector to assure that the most effective technologies are available to public safety agencies, to serve the safety of the public.

The initial phases of the FirstNet network deployment will most likely use LTE for transmitting data and video content only. Mission critical voice communications using standards designed for Land Mobile Radio (LMR) will be carried on separate networks. In time, many anticipate that IP standards for radios will replace LMR, bringing new economies of scale and higher levels of performance. The development of unified communications technologies to provide a national network places the nation on the path to achieve the long-sought goal of robust, interoperable communications for first responders.

KEY PROVISIONS IN THE SPECTRUM ACT TO IMPROVE PUBLIC SAFETY COMMUNICATIONS

A national program to provide nationwide coverage for public safety communications is to be developed and managed by a new federal entity, the First Responder Network Authority, or FirstNet. FirstNet has been established by the act and given broad powers to ensure that the nationwide public safety broadband network is built, maintained, and kept up-to-date as technology evolves. In consultation with federal, state, local, and tribal authorities, FirstNet will develop proposals to construct and manage the network with partners from the private sector, among others. Following is a discussion of major provisions in the act that pertain to public safety communications, including provisions to improve the nation's 911 emergency call system.

Among federal agencies designated by the act to provide consultation and support are the Federal Communications Commission (FCC), the National Telecommunications and Information Administration (NTIA), the National Institute of Standards and Technology (NIST), and the Office of Emergency Communications (OEC). The FCC manages commercial and non-federal spectrum use, including spectrum allocated to public safety. The NTIA manages federal spectrum resources and, along with NIST, is an agency within the Department of Commerce. OEC is part of the Office of Cybersecurity and Communications, Department of Homeland Security.

Spectrum Assignment

Radio frequency spectrum is an essential resource for wireless communications. The energy in electronic telecommunications transmissions converts airwaves into signals to deliver voice, text, and images. These signal frequencies are allocated for specific purposes, such as television broadcasting or WiFi,[6] and assigned to specific users through licenses. Allocating sufficient spectrum for wireless emergency communications has long been a concern for Congress. The Balanced Budget Act of 1997 (P.L. 105-33), for example, directed the FCC to allocate 24 MHz[7] of spectrum in the 700 MHz band for public safety use.[8]

With the passage of the Spectrum Act, some existing public safety licenses in the 700 MHz band[9] and an additional license (known as the D Block),[10] together totaling 22 MHz, have been designated by Congress to support a broadband communications network for public safety. As required by the act, the initial, 10-year license to use these frequencies was assigned by the FCC to FirstNet. It is renewable for an additional 10 years, on condition that FirstNet has met its duties and obligations under the act.[11]

A total of 34 MHz of spectrum capacity will therefore be available for public safety networks within the 700 MHz band: the 22 MHz designated for broadband, and 12 MHz allocated for narrowband communications, primarily voice.[12] Additionally, there are public safety networks on adjacent frequencies within the 800 MHz band. Time and technological advances may someday bring these spectrum assets together, but at present there are three distinct public safety network technologies in use or planned within the 700 MHz and 800 MHz bands. These are: broadband communications at 700 MHz; interoperable narrowband communications at 700 MHz; and narrowband communications at 800 MHz. Some of the narrowband networks at 700 MHz and 800 MHz can share infrastructure and radios but older narrowband networks at 800 MHz are often not easily integrated with narrowband networks being built on 700 MHz frequencies.

All of the 700 MHz band spectrum allocated for public safety use can support broadband networks. At present, however, there is no tested technology to deliver voice communications over LTE broadband that meets first responder requirements. The act gives the FCC the authority to "... allow the narrowband spectrum to be used in a flexible manner, including usage for public safety broadband communications.... "subject to technical and interference protection measures.[13] This provision might open an opportunity for early broadband network build-outs by public safety agencies that want to be in the vanguard of using LTE voice communications technology.

The act requires that public safety users return frequencies known as the T-Band.[14] These are frequencies between 470 and 512 MHz allocated for television that have been made available for public safety use in 11 urban areas.[15] Since the transition to digital television, radio transmissions on some of these frequency assignments have experienced interference and the public safety agencies that use them are considering moving to new networks at 700 MHz. Other areas have recently invested to upgrade networks built on the T-Band frequencies and are concerned about the loss of this communications capacity. The act requires that the FCC act by February 2021 to establish a relocation plan that would free up the T-Band for reassignment through competitive bidding. Proceeds from the auctions of T-Band frequencies are to be available for grants to cover relocation costs.[16] There are no requirements in the law as to how the NTIA, the designated grants administrator, is to structure the grant program or determine eligible costs, although the agency might decide to follow procedures for reallocating federal spectrum.

Some of the earliest spectrum assignments for public safety are in channels below 512 MHz. Public safety and other license-holders in designated channels below 512 MHz are required to reband their holdings to conform to an FCC mandate to improve spectrum efficiency.[17] This narrowbanding requirement, as it is called, requires that assigned channels be reduced from a width of 25 khz to 12.5 khz, thereby freeing up new spectrum capacity for public safety and other uses. The deadline to meet the narrowbanding requirement was January 1, 2013. To accommodate public safety license holders in the T-Band that now fall under requirements established in the act, the FCC has ruled to exempt them from the narrowbanding requirements.[18]

Although not specifically required by the act, several federal agencies have broad powers to undertake research and development that might further goals for improved performance of emergency communications systems, as well as more efficient and effective use of all spectrum resources allocated for public safety use. Many policy makers believe that additional technological development and planning should be undertaken, although FirstNet's mandate appears to limit it to the public safety broadband network to be operated on the spectrum licensed to it.

Expenditures and Revenue Sources

The cost of building a new wireless communications network is likely to be in the tens of billions of dollars.[19] To meet these costs, the expectation is that FirstNet will have access to existing infrastructure for some of the network's components and that it will be able to invest through partnerships—with commercial wireless carriers or other secondary users of its spectrum and infrastructure—that generate revenue.

The Spectrum Act provides over $7 billion in funding directed to FirstNet and to states, either as direct transfers or as grants. There is an initial loan of $2 billion (repayable from spectrum-license auction proceeds) to set up FirstNet and begin its operation.[20] The remaining $5 billion will become available as auctions for spectrum licenses are concluded and the revenues deposited in the Public Safety Trust Fund.

Public Safety Trust Fund

The law provides for transfers from a Public Safety Trust Fund, which is established in the Treasury by the act, to receive revenues from designated auctions of spectrum licenses.[21] The designated amounts are to remain available through FY2022, after which any remaining funds are to revert to the Treasury, to be used for deficit reduction. Auction proceeds are to be distributed in the following order of priority:

- To the NTIA, to reimburse the Treasury for funds advanced to cover the initial costs of establishing FirstNet: not to exceed $2 billion.
- To the State and Local Implementation Fund for a grant program: $135 million.
- To the Network Construction Fund for costs associated with building the nationwide network and for grants to states that qualify to build their own networks: $7 billion, reduced by the amount advanced to establish FirstNet.
- To NIST for public safety research: $100 million.
- To the Treasury for deficit reduction: $20.4 billion.
- To the NTIA and the National Highway Traffic Safety Administration for a grant program to improve 911 services: $115 million.
- To NIST for public safety research, phase two: $200 million.
- To the Treasury for deficit reduction: any remaining amounts from designated auction revenues.

Network Construction Fund

The Network Construction Fund is established in the Treasury to be used by FirstNet for expenditures on construction, maintenance, and related expenses to build the nationwide network required in the act; by the NTIA to make payments to states that are participating in FirstNet; and by the NTIA for grants to those states that qualify to build their own radio access network links.[22]

FirstNet: Limit on Expenditures

The act caps FirstNet's administrative expenses at $100 million in total over the first 10 years of operation. Costs attributed to oversight and audits are not included in the expense cap.[23]

FirstNet: Fee Income and Other Revenue

Congress gave FirstNet the authority to obtain grants, and to receive payment for the use of network capacity licensed to FirstNet and of network infrastructure "constructed, owned, or operated" by FirstNet.[24] Specifically, FirstNet is authorized to collect network user fees from public safety and secondary users[25] and to receive payments under leasing agreements in public-private partnerships.[26] These partnerships may be formed between FirstNet and a secondary user for the purpose of constructing, managing, and operating the network. The agreements may allow access to the network on a secondary basis for services other than public safety.[27] The act requires that these fees be sufficient each year to cover annual expenses of FirstNet to carry out required activities,[28] with any remaining revenue going to network construction, operation, maintenance, and improvement.[29] There is a prohibition on providing service directly to consumers; this does not impact the right to collect fees from a secondary user or enter into leasing agreements.[30]

State and Local Implementation Fund

The State and Local Implementation Fund was allocated $135 million from the Public Safety Trust Fund. The NTIA, which administers the grant program for this fund, may borrow up to the full amount.[31] The grants are to be made available to all 56 states and territories to develop a plan on how to use a nationwide public safety broadband network to meet their emergency communications needs. The program is to be established as a matching grant program. Federal grants from the fund are not to exceed 80% of the projected cost to the state, however, the NTIA may make the decision to waive the matching funds requirement.[32] The distribution of available funds among the states will be established by the NTIA in consultation with FirstNet.[33]

The NTIA subsequently decided to plan for funding in two phases. The first phase will provide funding for initial planning and related activities. The deadline for completed applications for phase one was March 19, 2013. The second phase will address states' needs in preparing for additional consulting with FirstNet, and for planning to undertake data collection activities.[34]

Expenditures by the NTIA from the State and Local Implementation Fund were reported at $300,000 for FY2012 for administrative costs. Disbursements for administrative costs and grants funding are estimated at $124,958,000 (base) for FY2013 and $9,700,000 for FY2014.[35]

The announced amount available for the first phase of grants from the fund is $121.5 million.[36] Grants totaling over $116 million were awarded to 54 of the 56 eligible states and territories in FY2013.[37] The state of Louisiana and the territory of the Northern Mariana Islands did not receive grants.[38] Many of the grants will be used to bolster existing state programs for public safety communications and interoperability, and for outreach and education.

Other Sources of Funds

The construction of this new network represents a significant investment for all participants. State public safety agencies have multiple obligations to build, upgrade, and equip other networks and may not be in a position to contribute to building and maintaining the new broadband network. The ability of FirstNet to procure funding from the private sector may be crucial to its success.

Planning Authority

The Spectrum Act created FirstNet as an independent entity within the NTIA. FirstNet is required to plan for and establish an interoperable broadband network for public safety. The act requires that state and local agencies and tribal authorities have a consulting role in the development, deployment, and operation of the nationwide network. The act further provides an opportunity for states to plan and build their own radio access networks within the framework of the nationwide broadband network.[39]

FirstNet

When Congress creates an independent entity within the federal government, it may have the obligation to achieve a specific goal, usually within a specific time frame.[40] As an independent entity, FirstNet—the First Responder Network Authority—has been given both goals and timeframes. It has been instructed by Congress to exercise all powers specifically granted by the act and "such incidental powers as shall be necessary"[41] to create a nationwide broadband network for public safety. Unless renewed, this authority expires in 2027.[42] The law requires FirstNet to become a self-funding entity, independent of government subsidies.[43] FirstNet is to take "all actions necessary to ensure the building, deployment, and operation" of the network in consultation with federal, state, tribal, and local public safety entities, the Director of NIST, the FCC, and the public safety advisory committee.[44] FirstNet appears therefore to be an autonomous organization, with broad powers to carry out its mandate, within the requirements established by the law. It has, for example, sole power to select the program's manager and its agents, consultants, and other experts subject to the requirement that they be chosen "in a fair, transparent, and objective manner."[45] However, FirstNet, except for certain exemptions provided in the act, must follow federal agency requirements, notably in hiring and procurement, slowing down the process for establishing FirstNet as a going concern.[46]

FirstNet is to be headed by a board of 15 members of which 12 are appointed by the Secretary of Commerce according to criteria established by the law, which are intended to provide both representation from key stakeholders and expertise. The other three members of the board are designees of the Secretary of the Department of Homeland Security, the Attorney General of the United States, and the Director of the Office of Management and Budget. The Secretary of Commerce is required to appoint a chairman of the board for an initial term of two years.[47] Initial appointments to the board were announced on August 20, 2012.[48]

As part of its management of the network, FirstNet is required, at a minimum:

- To establish network policies, including development of detailed requests for proposals to build the network, and operational matters such as terms of service and billing practices.[49]
- To consult with states on network-related expenditures, as part of the preparation of policies and requests for proposals.[50]

- To enter into agreements to use existing communications infrastructure, including commercial and federal infrastructure, "to the maximum extent economically desirable."[51]
- To ensure the construction, maintenance, operation, and improvement of the broadband network, taking into account new and evolving technologies.[52]
- To enter into agreements with commercial networks to allow public safety roaming on their networks.[53]
- To represent the interests of the network's users before standards-setting boards, in consultation with NIST, the FCC, and its own Public Safety Advisory Committee.[54]

FirstNet is required to create a public safety advisory committee to assist in carrying out its mandate.[55] There are no requirements in the statute as to the composition of the committee. Bylaws adopted at the organizing meeting of the First Net Board of Directors on September 25, 2012 created a Public Safety Advisory Committee.[56] It was further agreed that the members of the committee would be chosen from the Advisory Committee to SAFECOM, within the Department of Homeland Security, to be chosen in consultation with the Secretary of Homeland Security. The organizations chosen to be represented on the committee were announced on February 20, 2013.[57] State and local government interests are represented through a subcommittee of PSAC.

State and Local Participation

Every state has one or more agencies that plan for public safety, homeland security, and emergency communications. Most states have a Statewide Interoperability Coordinator (SWIC) to administer its Statewide Communication Interoperability Plan (SCIP).[58] SCIPs are written to conform with federal guidelines and requirements, such as the National Emergency Communications Plan. FirstNet is required to consult with regional, state, tribal, and local authorities regarding decisions such as those concerning the costs of the policies it formulates, as required in the law, including expenditures for the core network, placement of towers, coverage areas, security, and priority access for local users. Consultation will be through a state-selected coordinator as specified in the act.[59] Appointment of an individual or governmental body as the point-of-contact is also required as a condition of state participation and eligibility to receive grants established by the act.[60]

States may decide to use the existing SWIC as the required single point-of-contact or may choose to appoint a separate coordinator. Each state and other participants have successfully appointed a coordinator to work directly with FirstNet.[61]

The governor of each state is to be notified by FirstNet when it has completed its requests for proposals regarding construction, operation, maintenance, and improvement of a nationwide network. The governor or his designee will receive the details of the proposed plans and notification of the amount of funding available to the state if it participates in the FirstNet program.[62]

A state that does not want to participate in FirstNet's deployment plan for radio access networks must submit an alternative plan for construction, operation, maintenance, and improvement of the radio access network within the state. The state must demonstrate to the FCC, which the law requires to review the plan, that its planned radio access network would comply with minimum technical requirements and be interoperable with FirstNet. The state has 90 days to agree to participate or to notify FirstNet, the NTIA, and the FCC of its intent to deploy its own part of the radio access network, and an additional 180 days to provide its plan to the FCC.[63]

If the FCC does not approve the plan, the state might be obliged to participate in FirstNet.[64] If a state's plan is approved it will be eligible to apply for a grant, administered by the NTIA, that will be funded from the Network Construction Fund created by the act. The amount available may be less than what would have been provided if the state had opted in to the FirstNet program, because the grant will be applied only toward building the radio access network and may be subject to matching grant requirements. Approval of the grant is contingent on meeting additional requirements established by the NTIA, including sustainability, timeliness, cost-effectiveness, security, coverage, and services that are comparable to FirstNet.[65] The state would be required to pay a user fee for access to FirstNet's core network.[66] It would not be permitted to enter commercial markets or lease access to its network except through a public-private partnership. Any revenue to the state from a partnership must be used only for costs associated with its broadband network.[67]

Some industry observers have expressed concern about the impact on the success of the nationwide broadband network if many states choose to build their own radio access networks. The cost to FirstNet of building the nationwide network may go up, for example, if anticipated economies of scale are diminished. It may be more difficult for FirstNet to negotiate the partnerships that are expected to provide much of the needed funding for the network. A state that has its plans approved by the FCC may not be able to meet stipulated requirements when its network is built; absent any action by the FCC to enforce technical requirements, the goal of seamless interoperability across all broadband systems may be jeopardized. States operating within and outside the FirstNet deployment plan may, over time, have difficulty in finding the funds to complete radio access network build-outs, leaving significant gaps in what is intended to be nationwide coverage.

The act only identifies two options for a state: join FirstNet or build a statewide radio access network subject to the provisions of the act. The act does not include specific provisions for a state that chooses to build its own radio access network without opting out of FirstNet, although providing such an option may be within FirstNet's charter. A state might, for example, choose to build its own data management center or mobile access routers while also sharing FirstNet's infrastructure for regional and national coverage. The act also is silent on whether states may choose to opt-out of the broadband network entirely, choosing neither to join FirstNet nor to build a broadband network on the frequencies assigned to FirstNet. Some states may prefer to concentrate their resources on improving mission-critical voice networks and acquire broadband access from a commercial provider or through other means.

On the other hand, there are many benefits for independent action by individual states and regional partnerships of two or more states. For example, LTE networks are relying increasing on small cell architectures[68] that are organized around local nodes. This configuration might correspond with local jurisdictions, potentially providing better interoperability with the core network, while reducing capital investment in infrastructure. One advantage for states building their own radio access networks on FirstNet spectrum is that they will have greater control over any partnerships formed and on expenditures within their states. Although the act requires states to use any revenue from partnerships only to cover costs associated with the state's network, the states will be able to make their own decisions about priorities, with more confidence that revenues will be available when needed.

Although there are many potential benefits for states to participate in a nationwide network, such as economies of scale, more secure and robust communications, and a unified base for collaborative efforts, there are also a number of risks, especially if FirstNet fails to deliver promised benefits. The success of FirstNet as an accepted planning authority and leader may depend on whether it makes a compelling business case in the requests for proposals required by the act.

FirstNet's plans for partnerships with the private sector and the nature of the network development plans proposed to each state may be of particular interest to Congress as an early indicator of the viability of FirstNet in meeting the goals required by the act.

Federal Governance

Federal governance of the nationwide public safety broadband network, as required by the Spectrum Act, is primarily through consultation and oversight. Planning, investment, operations, and other related decisions are to be made by the FirstNet board and the experts it is to hire on a permanent or consultative basis.

Statutory Obligations

Examples of statutory obligations for Congress and the Administration in the direction of FirstNet include the following.

Membership on FirstNet board. The members of the FirstNet board are to be chosen by the Secretary of Commerce, within the parameters established in the act. The Department of Homeland Security, the Attorney General, and the Office of Management and Budget each have one member on the board in permanence. The Secretary of Commerce is required to appoint a chairman of the board for an initial term of two years.[69]

Grant programs for planning. The NTIA is to establish and administer the State and Local Implementation Fund. Grant provisions are to be decided in consultation with FirstNet,[70] but not necessarily in accordance with decisions made by the FirstNet board and executive management.

Grant programs for state networks. The NTIA is to administer grants from the Network Construction Fund to states that qualify to build their own radio access networks and choose to apply for a grant.[71]

Funding for FirstNet and participating states through the Network Construction Fund. The NTIA is to determine the funding level available to each state for the buildout of the nationwide broadband network, if the state chooses to participate in FirstNet.[72]

Spectrum leases for state networks. The NTIA sets the terms and is responsible for enforcing the requirement that states qualifying to build their radio access networks must sublease spectrum through FirstNet, the assigned license-holder.[73]

License review. The FCC is required to review the initial 10-year license assigned to FirstNet and consider its renewal based on performance criteria.[74]

Performance review. The Government Accountability Office (GAO), within 10 years, is to prepare a report providing recommendations on "what action Congress should take" regarding the mandated termination of authority of FirstNet in 2027.[75]

Fee schedule. The NTIA is to review and approve the annual schedule of fees charged to public safety agencies and other users for access to FirstNet's resources.[76]

Annual audit. The Secretary of Commerce is to contract for an annual audit of FirstNet's finances and activities. The reports are to be submitted to Congress, the President, and FirstNet.[77]

Report to Congress. FirstNet is required to submit annual reports to Congress on its "operations, activities, financial conditions, and accomplishments."[78]

The designated appropriate congressional committees are, in the Senate, the Committee on Commerce, Science, and Transportation; in the House, the Committee on Energy and Commerce.[79] These committees and other committees with jurisdiction are likely to take an active role in oversight, many believe.

Although there are several platforms for oversight and guidance provided in the act, it seems likely that the primary, day-to-day responsibility for monitoring progress will fall to the NTIA. Agency discretion for funding states that participate in FirstNet and for providing grants to states that opt out is authorized by the act. The $7 billion grant to the Network Construction Fund is implicitly divided into three parts: one funding FirstNet to establish the network; one funding states that participate in FirstNet; and one funding states that choose to opt out. Clauses that may have been intended to oversee state expenditures might be construed by the NTIA to include FirstNet. The act, however, does not provide guidance to the NTIA on how to balance fiduciary caution with entrepreneurial initiative in assuring a flow of funds to FirstNet.

Public-Private Partnerships

Partnerships are expected to play a critical role in building and operating the network. Electric utility companies, for example, are upgrading their networks to meet Smart Grid requirements,[80] and some companies have expressed an interest in partnering with FirstNet or state authorities. Some commercial wireless service providers have also expressed an interest in working in partnership with public safety entities to develop and operate new broadband networks.

The Spectrum Act requires FirstNet to issue "open, transparent, and competitive" requests for proposals to private sector entities for building, operating, and maintaining the network[81] that leverage to the extent "economically desirable" existing commercial wireless infrastructure, in order to expedite network deployment.[82] It is charged with managing and overseeing the resulting contracts or agreements. As part of a separate requirement to assure substantial rural coverage during all phases of deployment, the act requires that industry proposals and contracts include, if possible, partnerships with existing commercial mobile providers.[83]

Decisions by FirstNet about the network's design, construction, and operation are likely to have a significant impact on commercial participation in a public safety broadband network or networks. These decisions may also influence decision-making by states as to whether or not to pursue radio area network construction independently or through their own partnerships.

Congress may be interested in the composition of private sector partnerships formed by FirstNet and individual states, not only for their business plans but also for the inclusion of a wide variety of stakeholders. For example, are rural and tribal wireless carriers included as business partners? Do secondary access agreements support services that meet social goals, such as for telemedicine, or are they exclusively for commercial purposes? Is competition in providing wireless services being enhanced or hindered?

Infrastructure

Infrastructure for the new network includes operations centers, towers, antennae, base stations, routers, small cell nodes, and other communications equipment, as well as radios and the software that links them to the network. For wireless communications, an important infrastructure component is the connection between base stations and communications backbones. These networks, which usually operate over fiber-optic cable or microwave connection, are typically referred to as backhaul.

The Spectrum Act requires FirstNet to establish a nationwide, interoperable public safety network.[84] Network infrastructure components that are specifically required include

- Core network of national and regional data centers and other elements, all based on commercial standards.
- Connectivity between the radio access network and the public Internet or the Public Switched Telephone Network, or both.
- Network cell site equipment, antennas, and backhaul equipment, based on commercial standards, to support wireless devices operating on frequencies designated for public safety broadband.[85]

FirstNet is required to leverage existing infrastructure by entering into agreements to use commercial or other communications infrastructure, including federal, state, tribal, or local infrastructure.[86] Planned phases for infrastructure deployment are to include "substantial rural coverage."[87]

FirstNet's ability to build the required network may depend on the timeliness, scope, and outcome of its negotiations to share infrastructure with other parties in order to focus resources on providing elements deemed essential for public safety use of broadband communications.

Timeframe

The requirements of the Spectrum Act must be substantially met and the viability of the project demonstrated no later than the end of FY2022, if not sooner. The State and Local Implementation Fund and the Network Construction Fund expire in 2022, with any balances reverting to the Treasury. By 2022, the GAO must have assessed the performance of FirstNet and provided a report to Congress; and the FCC must decide whether or not to renew the licenses for the public safety broadband network. Within this 10-year timeframe, there are few deadlines beyond requirements for the initial establishment of the planning and implementation framework.

Many of the important steps for building the network have no required deadline. Some milestones, such as rural coverage, are mandated in the act, but the deadlines are not specified. There are, for example, no deadlines in provisions that require FirstNet to:

- Develop requests for proposals that include a requirement for timetables.[88]
- Consult with states on establishing state and local planning processes.[89]
- Complete the request for proposal process that is to be given to each state governor regarding the request for proposal and its details, and the funding level for each state as determined by the NTIA.[90]

Mandated deadlines for states include

- Within 90 days of receipt of notice from FirstNet, the governor shall choose either to participate in deployment of FirstNet or to conduct its own radio access network deployment within the state.[91]
- Within 180 days of giving notice to opt out of FirstNet, the governor shall complete requests for proposals for a state network.[92]

No deadline is established in the statute for the FCC to approve or disapprove state proposals for their own portion of the nationwide broadband network.[93] There are also no specified deadlines for a state to apply to the NTIA for a grant to construct the radio access network and to lease spectrum capacity from First Net, if FCC approval is received for a state network.[94] However, one condition of eligibility for a grant to a state to build its own radio access network is that the state's plan must demonstrate "the ability to complete the project within specified comparable deadlines.... "[95]

FirstNet and the FCC may need to be expeditious in completing all steps for the preparation, review, and acceptance of requests for proposals so that construction of the required core network begins in a timely manner. Too many delays in administrative processes may erode the feasibility of the project.

The FirstNet Board may opt to provide additional requirements for timelines and goals that coordinate their own efforts with those of the FCC, the NTIA, state agencies, and other stakeholders. In particular, consideration may be given to modifying timelines to accommodate states' own time lines, for example, for budget approvals.

Next Generation 9-1-1

Today's 911 system is built on an infrastructure of analog technology that does not support many of the features that most Americans expect to be part of an emergency response. Efforts to splice newer, digital technologies onto this aging infrastructure have created points of failure where a call can be dropped or misdirected, sometimes with tragic consequences. Callers to 911, however, generally assume that the newer technologies they are using to place a call are matched by the same level of technology at the 911 call centers, known as Public Safety Answering Points (PSAPs). However, this is not always the case. To modernize the system to provide the quality of service that approaches the expectations of its users will require that the PSAPs and state, local, and possibly federal emergency communications authorities invest in new technologies. As envisioned by most stakeholders, these new technologies—collectively referred to as Next Generation 911 or NG9-1-1—should incorporate Internet Protocol standards. An IP-enabled emergency communications network that supports 911 will facilitate interoperability and system resilience; improve connections between 911 call centers; provide more robust capacity; and offer flexibility in receiving and managing calls. The same network can also serve wireless broadband communications for public safety and other emergency personnel, as well as other purposes.

Recognizing the importance of providing effective 911 service, Congress has previously passed three major bills supporting improvements in the handling of 911 emergency calls. The Wireless Communications and Public Safety Act of 1999 (P.L. 106-81) established 911 as the number to call for emergencies and gave the Federal Communications Commission (FCC) authority to regulate many aspects of the service. The most recent of these laws, the NET 911 Improvement Act of 2008 (P.L. 110-283), required the preparation of a National Plan for migrating to an IPenabled emergency network. Responsibility for the plan was assigned to the E-911 Implementation Coordination Office (ICO), created to meet requirements of an earlier law, the ENHANCE 911 Act of 2004 (P.L. 108-494). Authorization for the ICO terminated on September 30, 2009. ICO was jointly administered by the National Telecommunications and Information Administration and the National Highway Traffic Safety Administration.

Spectrum Act provisions re-establish the federal 9-1-1 Implementation Coordination Office (ICO) to advance planning for next-generation systems and to administer a grant program.[96] ICO is to provide matching grants to eligible state or local governments or tribal organizations for the implementation, operation, and migration of various types of 911 and IP-enabled emergency services, and for public safety personnel training.[97] States that have diverted fees collected for 911 services are not eligible for grants under the program.[98] Based on the act's prioritized plan for funding programs with spectrum license auction revenue, the funds for the grant program will be made available only after $27.635 billion of available auction revenue has been applied to other purposes.

Provisions in the act regarding 911 programs include

- The GAO is required to study how states assess fees on 911 services and how those fees are used.[99]
- The General Services Administration is required to prepare a report on 911 capabilities of multi-line telephone systems in federal facilities and the FCC is to seek comment on the feasibility of improving 911 identification for calls placed through multi-line telephone systems.[100]
- The FCC is to assess the legal and regulatory environment for development of NG9-1-1 and barriers to that development, including state regulatory roadblocks.[101] The FCC is also to (1) initiate a proceeding to create a specialized Do-Not-Call registry for public safety answering points, and (2) to establish penalties and fines for autodialing (robocalls) and related violations.[102]
- ICO, in consultation with NHTSA and DHS is to report on costs for requirements and specifications of NG9-1-1 services, including an analysis of costs, and assessments and analyses of technical uses.[103]
- Immunity and liability protections are provided—to the extent consistent with specified provisions of the Wireless Communications and Public Safety Act of 1999—for various users and providers of Next Generation 911 and related services, including for the release of subscriber information.[104]

The act also requires FirstNet to promote integration of the nationwide public safety broadband network with PSAPs.[105] Since the NTIA has responsibilities for both ICO and FirstNet, the agency is in a position to encourage interoperability between PSAPs and First Responders as they move to common IP-based platforms.

Technology and Standards

Standardization of network components, including radios, is generally considered essential to achieving interoperability, improving service, and reducing operating costs. Technical requirements for FirstNet are to be based on commercial standards for LTE.[106] The commercial sector has begun the transition to operating on IP-enabled networks such as LTE. Wireless carriers around the world are installing LTE networks for consumers and planning for the next generation of LTE: LTE Advanced.[107] LTE Advanced technologies will be able to operate across noncontiguous spectrum bands, thereby increasing channel widths for greater capacity and performance. Most experts agree that LTE Advanced will facilitate the transition to new technologies by making it easier and less expensive to phase out older infrastructure.

To expedite the expansion of LTE, commercial carriers have often relied on Wide Area Network (WAN) installations and configurations of small cells to create what are commonly referred to as micro networks. The micro networks operate on standards for LTE and IEEE (Institute of Electrical and Electronics Engineers) 802.11 for WiFi. Micro networks may become a key component of FirstNet, as they represent an opportunity to add capacity at a local level in times of emergency.

FirstNet

The Spectrum Act requires FirstNet to assure nationwide standards for use of and access to the network it is tasked with developing. The act specifies the use of commercial standards for some of the network components.[108]

To promote competition, devices for public safety network radios and other wireless devices are required to be built to open, non-proprietary, commercially available standards, "capable of being used by any public safety entity and by multiple vendors across all broadband networks operating in the 700 MHz band" and backward compatible with existing commercial networks where necessary and reasonable.[109]

FCC

The act required the FCC to establish a Technical Advisory Board for First Responder Interoperability, and set out criteria for the selection and participation of board members.[110] The primary purpose of the board was to agree on minimum technical requirements for nationwide interoperability on the public safety broadband network. The Interoperability Board was required to develop these technical recommendations in consultation with the NTIA,

NIST, and the OEC.[111] The board's technical recommendations were required to be based on commercial standards for LTE.[112] The establishment of minimum technical requirements has a two-fold purpose. One, the requirements are to be presented to the Board of Directors of FirstNet as recommended requirements for interoperability.[113] Two, the minimum technical requirements are to be used by the FCC as a standard of interoperability for evaluating state plans in cases where states have asked to build their own radio access networks.[114]

In the report it submitted,[115] the Interoperability Board, in addition to minimum technical standards, also provided additional considerations that it judged to be important for achieving interoperability.

NIST

The Director of NIST, in consultation with the FCC, DHS, and the National Institute of Justice, Department of Justice, is to "conduct research and assist with the development of standards, technologies and applications to advance wireless public safety communications."[116] More specifically, in consultation with FirstNet and the Public Safety Advisory Committee, NIST is to

- Document technical requirements for public safety wireless communications.
- Accelerate the development of interoperability between currently deployed systems and the public safety broadband network.
- Establish a research plan and direct research for next-generation wireless public safety needs.
- Accelerate the development of broadband network features such as mission-critical voice, prioritization, and authentication.
- Accelerate the development of communications equipment and technology to facilitate the eventual migration of public safety narrowband communications to the public safety broadband network.[117]

Furthermore, the Director of NIST, in consultation with FirstNet and the FCC, "shall ensure the development of a list of certified devices and components meeting appropriate protocols and standards for public safety and commercial vendors."[118]

Need for Standards Development

Narrowband and broadband networks for public safety will by most accounts be incompatible with each other and with other networks for the foreseeable future.[119] Only a small part of the existing public safety infrastructure is expected to be usable in the development of new networks at 700 MHz. To maximize the utility of new investments in infrastructure and radios, many believe that standards that support public safety applications for IP-enabled technologies must be completed in the early stages of planning and building. Just as access to the Internet has revolutionized business and social cultures worldwide, the transition to IP-enabled networks is likely to expand the capability and scope of emergency communications.

The act variously requires NIST, the FCC, and the NTIA[120] to develop standards and take steps to improve spectrum efficiency and support the development of the next generation of wireless technology. These agencies already have a number of initiatives in place, notably the Public Safety Communications Research program (PSCR). PSCR provides research, development, and testing to advance public safety communications interoperability. The program is a joint effort between NIST's Office of Law Enforcement Standards and NTIA's Institute for Telecommunication Sciences and is sponsored by the Office for Interoperability and Compatibility at DHS, and the Department of Justice Community Oriented Policing Services.[121]

The funding for the federal research and development efforts described in the act is provided from spectrum license auction revenue. The timing of the auctions and the prioritization for distributing auction revenues are such that the funds designated for research and development may not be available for several years, if at all. Some of the act's provisions require the FCC to auction designated spectrum within three years.[122] The first of these auctions, Auction 96, was completed on February 27, 2014, with a total winning bid of $1.564 billion.[123] The first round of funding for NIST ($100 million) would occur once the proceeds from spectrum license auctions deposited in the Public Safety Trust Fund surpass $7.135 billion. The second funding round for NIST would occur after deposits reach $27.75 billion. Although resources in existing federal programs may be shifted to give priority to the implementation of the Middle Class Tax Relief and Job Creation Act of 2012,[124] the federal government may not be able to fund all of the standards and other technological research that is required by the act or needed for public safety. Timely development of public safety applications and standards may come primarily from the private sector, where some vendors are developing components needed for the broadband network and its devices. To meet its responsibilities under the act, FirstNet may choose to allocate some of the funding provided to it by the act, or raise additional funds, to facilitate standards development.

If no solution is found to coordinate private and public work on standards development and new technologies for emergency communications, the development of IP-enabled technologies for public safety may continue to lag behind that of the commercial sector, perpetuating the high costs and inefficiencies that have plagued first responder communications for decades.

ROAMING AND PRIORITY ACCESS WITHIN THE 700 MHZ BAND

In its *National Broadband Plan*, the FCC indicated that it wanted to make commercial networks in the 700 MHz band available for public safety use and requested that Congress confirm the FCC's authority to act.[125] The Spectrum Act provides the FCC with statutory authority to establish rules in the public interest to improve the ability of public safety networks to roam on commercial space and to gain priority access.[126]

FirstNet is empowered by the act to enter into agreements with commercial providers that would allow public safety network users to roam on partnering networks.[127] The act does not state whether roaming agreements may be negotiated by states that opt-out and receive spectrum leases from the NTIA to operate their own radio access networks. Agreements might also cover rules for priority access in times of high demand for network capacity. Priority access can take several forms, such as "ruthless pre-emption," in which non-public-safety transmissions are immediately terminated to make way for emergency communications, or negotiated priority agreements that might, for example, place public safety users at the head of the line for network access as capacity becomes available. The act stipulates that the FCC's authority may not require roaming or priority access unless (1) the public safety and commercial networks are technically compatible; (2) the commercial network is reasonably compensated; and (3) access does not preempt or otherwise terminate or degrade existing traffic on the commercial network.[128] Within these limits, the FCC appears to have some leeway to use its regulatory authority to support public safety in negotiations with partners. The FCC cannot, under the act, mandate ruthless pre-emption, although the act does not preclude contractual negotiations that would allow it.

The act's provisions for roaming and priority access do not require a commercial vendor to make additional investments to insure technical compatibility, and the act's language might be interpreted as precluding an FCC mandate to that effect. Interpretation and enforcement of the compatibility provision may pose an obstacle to achieving desired levels of network interoperability and cross-network roaming because existing technical standards for the 700 MHz band might preclude affordable full-spectrum roaming, that is, the ability of any network within the 700 MHz to roam on any other network within the 700 MHz band. Full-spectrum roaming is considered by many to provide advantages for public safety and also for the public at large. For example, it makes more network capacity available for shared emergency communications of all types, not just for first responders. Many believe that full-spectrum access supports competitiveness among wireless carriers—in particular assisting small wireless carriers serving rural areas to offer new broadband services—by providing access to all customers within the band.

Achieving full-spectrum roaming on the 700 MHz band requires modifications of technical requirements for LTE, the preferred technology for mobile broadband within the 700 MHz band. The FCC has taken actions in support of full-spectrum roaming,[129] including steps to implement a voluntary industry agreement to establish interoperability for LTE in the lower 700 MHz band.[130] Establishing additional standards to enable full-spectrum interoperability will permit interoperability among all commercial carriers and public safety agencies.

FIRSTNET STATUS REPORT FOR 2013

The Chairman of FirstNet, Samuel Ginn, provided testimony on FirstNet's progress at a hearing on November 21, 2013.[131] Mr. Ginn prefaced his testimony with a strong statement that FirstNet holds full responsibility for its own success. He went on to describe the efforts of the board members who did double duty to compensate for the delayed hiring of key employees. Senior management positions that were filled beginning in spring 2013 include a General Manager, Deputy General Manager, Chief Financial Officer, Chief Counsel, Chief of Staff, and Chief Administrative Officer. During the interim period, the board focused, in particular, on outreach to states, negotiations with BTOP grant recipients, and development of policies and practices for self-governance. These activities continue and expand as new staff are brought on board.

In June 2013, Requests for Information regarding separate aspects of FirstNet technical requirements and strategies for implementation were issued. The information provided by the 285 responses is providing a resource for developing partnerships and preparing the Requests for Proposals that will lead to the building of FirstNet.

Mr. Ginn provided Congress with a list of FirstNet's priorities for FY2014. These were described as:

- Network Partnerships. Explore and validate a wide variety of partnership opportunities.
- Requests for Information. Evaluate the responses to 10 RFIs that covered topics in two main categories: Radio Access Networks, which includes network partnering and providers, antenna systems, microwave backhaul equipment, mobile network solutions, satellites; and Core Network, which includes enhanced packet core, transmission/transport, data center, network management center/operations management center, network service platforms.
- Core Network. Assure that the core network meets high standards for security, operations, and business support.
- State Consultation and Plans. Identify full service and support opportunities, device procurement, and network service fees. Explain the role of FirstNet and its responsibilities to each state.
- Integration of BTOP Projects. Leverage BTOP's public safety grant programs to establish market-based deployments of the nationwide network that will demonstrate its benefits and capabilities to public safety jurisdictions across the country.
- Mobile Network Solutions. Evaluate and plan for deployable network infrastructure to supplement or replace fixed infrastructure such as cell towers. Explore the potential of a variety of deployable infrastructure technologies, that might include satellite, microwave, balloons, and Unmanned Aerial Vehicles (drones).
- Wireless Devices. Assure that public safety agencies will have a portfolio of broadband LTE devices, built to open standards. Leverage FirstNet's national scale and open standards to significantly reduce device price points.

Mr. Ginn testified that the issue of controlling costs is a key factor in the success of the network. This means, for example, competitive pricing for FirstNet's services to states and tribal nations, low-cost mobile devices, and leveraging investments in infrastructure through partnerships.

Mr. Ginn stated that FirstNet's "objective is to develop long-standing relationships with public safety at every level." To support state local, and tribal emergency response and recovery communications needs, FirstNet plans to establish 10 regional offices that align with the regional offices of the Federal Emergency Management Agency.[132]

FirstNet engages with its federal partners through the Emergency Communications Preparedness Center[133] and individual agencies.

CONSIDERATIONS FOR CONGRESS

Congress may wish to examine the environment in which FirstNet is operating to see if it can be improved to help assure FirstNet's success in the efficient establishment of a nationwide network, such as assuring continuity of operations, and establishing self-funding measures for investment and operations.

Evolving Network Technologies

In the two years since the Spectrum Act was passed, communications technologies have evolved in ways not fully anticipated at the time.[134] Advances in small cell technology, in particular, are moving traffic management away from the core of cell tower infrastructure and toward micro networks built on the principles of Wide Area Networks. These micro networks are local in nature but fully interoperable across wide geographic areas.

FirstNet's decision to create ten regional offices meets both governance needs and the likely organization of FirstNet's nationwide infrastructure. The regional structure takes advantage of new networking solutions that can build on existing deployments of broadband networks. Every firehouse, 911 call center, police station, and other public structure, including lampposts and traffic lights, might be a link in a micro network. In this environment, the integration of Next Generation 911 infrastructure with FirstNet becomes a crucial part of network deployment strategy.[135]

Governance

Congress may also wish to address concerns about who is responsible for deploying the broadband network. Some of the reported confusion among potential partners about FirstNet's plans for the future[136] may stem from the different positions about network development taken by FirstNet's management and the NTIA. Both have expressed views about the nature of FirstNet, with the NTIA favoring centralized control of the network, led by the Department of Commerce, and FirstNet moving toward a network structure that treats states as equal partners.

In helping to stand up FirstNet, NTIA administrators have, apparently, chosen to treat FirstNet as if it were to exist within the Department of Commerce in perpetuity.[137] Treating FirstNet as a division of the Department of Commerce might be described as setting a course for FirstNet to become "another Amtrak," a term used by many, within and outside Congress,[138] to denote overdependence on federal subsidies, as in the case of financial support for Amtrak.[139] However, the governance structure of Amtrak is not the source of Amtrak's financial woes. Most policy makers believe that weak consumer demand and market regulations have contributed to Amtrak's failure to be a profitable corporation, even though it was intended as such at the time of its formation.

Amtrak

Amtrak, originally known as the National Railroad Passenger Corporation (NRPC), was created by the Rail Passenger Service Act of 1970 (P.L. 91-518). The purpose of the act was "to provide financial assistance for, and establishment of, a national rail passenger system, to provide for the modernization of railroad passenger equipment ..." and related purposes,[140] in response to a perceived "threat that railroad passenger service might disappear throughout the country."[141]

The NRPC was established by Congress as a private, for-profit corporation, not as an entity of the federal government. Nonetheless, eight of the 15 members of the board of directors were to be appointed by the president, with the remainder chosen to represent shareholders. The corporation was required to issue both common and preferred stock. A 15-member advisory panel was established to advise the board on ways to increase capitalization. The NRPC received a combination of direct appropriations and loan guarantees, including direct loans or guarantees to railroads entering into contracts with the NRPC, in order to be relieved of their obligations to provide passenger service. Subsequent legislation – in 1972, 1973, 1974, and 1975 – created a form of public service corporation whose primary objective is to serve the public convenience and necessity.[142]

Conrail

To address continuing problems in the railroad industry, the Regional Rail Reorganization Act of 1973 (P.L. 93-236) created the Consolidated Rail Corporation (Conrail) as a for-profit corporation. Conrail was authorized and directed by Congress, in brief:[143]

- To acquire rail properties.
- To operate rail service.
- To rehabilitate and improve rail properties.
- To maintain adequate and efficient rail service.

To capitalize the business, Conrail was authorized to issue common stock, among other provisions in the act that addressed financing. As long as 50% or more of Conrail's debt was owed to or backed by the federal government, it was obliged to maintain federal representation on its board and was subject to the Government Corporation Control Act for auditing purposes. Beginning in 1987, Conrail sold its assets to the private sector, with the proceeds going to the Treasury. The private sector also acquired Conrail's public obligations as a common carrier.

Although there are some differences between the governance structures, Conrail succeeded where Amtrak struggled in large part due to growing demand for freight traffic contrasted with diminishing demand for passenger rail service.

FirstNet

Although public safety communications are considered essential, as was rail passenger service when the NRPC was created, the wireless communications industry is vibrant and growing, whereas the railroad industry was in a chaotic state after the bankruptcy of the Penn Central Railroad.

To fund its operations, FirstNet is encouraged by the act to create public-private partnerships. The language of the Spectrum Act appears to have given FirstNet a mandate to have established itself as an ongoing, self-funding organization by 2022. These provisions, among others, suggest that Congress was seeking to establish an entity that might be more like Conrail than Amtrak. Absent specific instructions, stakeholders would appear to have some influence in deciding whether FirstNet—a unique hybrid—will be closer to being an Amtrak or a Conrail.

The act's provisions regarding FirstNet's operations are consistent with Congress's decision to provide a goal—the creation of a new communications network service for public safety—and set a deadline for the achievement of the goal. To achieve this goal, FirstNet might benefit from the maximum leeway in its operations, consistent with twin mandates for inclusive governance (such as states and public safety agencies at all levels) and private sector partnerships that invest in the network by making available infrastructure and other capital investments.

Assessment by the GAO

Before the end of FY2022, GAO is to recommend to Congress what actions should be taken in regard to the end of FirstNet's authority, which the act mandated to occur in 2027, 15 years after the passage of the act.

Options for GAO recommendations regarding governance may include:

- Federal corporation with the authority to issue bonds not backed by the federal government, and that, in time, becomes self-sustaining; the Tennessee Valley Authority (TVA) might provide an example of how such a charter might evolve.[144]
- Hybrid corporation established by the federal government, relying on a combination of earned income and federal funding, such as Amtrak.
- Corporation established by the federal government, such as Conrail. The federal presence on the Conrail board was tied to repayment of federal obligations.
- Federal corporation established as a transition vehicle to transfer to the private sector, such as the U.S. Enrichment Corporation.
- Federal agency in perpetuity either as an entity within the NTIA or through some other federal governance structure.

These potential choices will likely be influenced by decisions made by FirstNet's board and management team, and by the NTIA through the grant process and the policies it establishes.

In its oversight of FirstNet, Congress may wish to consider the impact of decisions made today on the probable future outcome for FirstNet. Business organization and technology choices are often closely linked; businesses that revise their management and production structures to incorporate new technology tend to be more productive.[145] Therefore, governance choices for FirstNet may help the authority to be more efficient and effective if they fully accommodate new technologies. An example is the announcement by AT&T of plans that are predicted to "transform the wide area network" and reduce capital expenditures.[146]

In light of what is likely to become a significant shift in wireless network technology, a preliminary analysis of FirstNet by the GAO might lead to recommendations for how to mesh current business plans for the new network with a transition strategy for possible future governance structures.

End Notes

[1] Discussed in Congressional Research Service General Distribution Memorandum, "Communications Support for Public Safety: The 9/11 Commission Report and Alternative Approaches," by Linda K. Moore, August 25, 2004, and in CRS Report RL31375, Emergency Communications: Meeting Public Safety Spectrum Needs by Linda K. Moore, 2002- 2003 (out of print; available from the author).

[2] Some of the actions by Congress and by federal agencies were summarized in testimony by Linda K. Moore, Specialist in Telecommunications Policy, Congressional Research Service, before the House Committee on Homeland Security, Subcommittee on Emergency Preparedness, Response, and Communications, "Ensuring Coordination and Cooperation: A Review of Emergency Communications Offices Within the Department of Homeland Security," November 17, 2011. The GAO has also addressed these issues in reports such as Emergency Communications: Various Challenges Likely to Slow Implementation of a Public Safety Broadband Network, February 2012, GAO-12-343 at http://www.gao.gov/assets/590/588795.pdf. CRS reports on the topic include CRS Report R41842, Funding Emergency Communications: Technology and Policy Considerations; CRS Report R40859, Public Safety Communications and Spectrum Resources: Policy Issues for Congress; CRS Report RL34054, Public-Private Partnership for a Public Safety Network: Governance and Policy; CRS Report RL33838, Emergency Communications: Policy Options at a Crossroads, all by Linda K. Moore.

[3] P.L. 112-96, Section 6202 (b).

[4] P.L. 112-96, Section 6203 (c) (2).

[5] "Directions for future cellular mobile network architecture," by Byoung-Jo J. Kim and Paul S. Henry, First Monday: Peer-Reviewed Journal on the Internet, December 3, 2012, http://firstmonday.org/ojs/index.php/fm/article/view/4204.

[6] WiFi, for wireless fidelity, operates on unlicensed frequencies that are not assigned to a specific owner but instead are available to support any device approved by the FCC.

[7] Spectrum is segmented into bands of radio frequencies and typically measured in cycles per second, or hertz. Standard abbreviations for measuring frequencies include kHz—kilohertz

or thousands of hertz; MHz—megahertz, or millions of hertz; and GHz—gigahertz, or
billions of hertz. The 700 MHz band includes radio frequencies from 698 MHz to 806 MHz.

[8] 47 U.S.C. §309 (j) (14).

[9] 763-768 MHz, 793-798 MHz, 768-769 MHz and 798-799 MHz.

[10] 758-763 MHz and 788-793 MHz; P.L. 112-96, Section 6001, (2).

[11] P.L. 112-96, Section 6201.

[12] 769-775 MHz and 799-805 MHz.

[13] P.L. 112-96, Section 6102.

[14] P.L. 112-96, Section 6103.

[15] Metropolitan areas: Boston, MA, Chicago, IL, Dallas/Fort Worth, TX, Houston, TX, Los
Angeles, CA, Miami, FL, New York, NY/Newark NJ, Philadelphia, PA, Pittsburgh, PA,
San Francisco/Oakland, CA, and Washington, DC.

[16] The National Public Safety Telecommunications Council (NPSTC) prepared a report that
provided an overview of T-Band assignments, some of the problems created by the act's
requirements, and possible alternative solutions. NPSTC, T-Band Report, March 15, 2013;
link to PDF at http://www.npstc.org/, "NPSTC Releases T Band Report."

[17] Details at http://transition.fcc.gov/pshs/public-safety-spectrum/narrowbanding.html.

[18] FCC, "Waiver of Narrowbanding Deadlines for T-Band (470-512 MHz) Licenses," Docket No.
WT 99-87, released April 26, 2012.

[19] Some cost estimates for building and operating a public safety broadband network are provided
in CRS Report R41842, Funding Emergency Communications: Technology and Policy
Considerations, by Linda K. Moore.

[20] P.L. 112-96, Section 6207.

[21] P.L. 112-96, Section 6413.

[22] P.L. 112-96, Section 6206 (e).

[23] P.L. 112-96, Section 6207 (b).

[24] P.L. 112-96, Section 6206 (b) (4).

[25] P.L. 112-96, Section 6208 (a) (1).

[26] P.L. 112-96, Section 6208 (a) (2).

[27] P.L. 112-96, Section 6208 (a) (2) (B).

[28] P.L. 112-96, Section 6208 (b).

[29] P.L. 112-96, Section 6208 (d).

[30] P.L. 112-96, Section 6212.

[31] P.L. 112-96, Section 6301.

[32] P.L. 112-96, Section 6302 (b).

[33] P.L. 112-96, Section 6302 (a).

[34] Announcement of Federal Funding Opportunity at http://www.ntia.doc.gov/files/ntia/
publications/sligp_ffo_02062013.pdf.

[35] U.S. Department of Commerce, National Telecommunications and Information
Administration, FY2014 Budget as Presented to Congress, April 2013; State and Local
Implementation Fund, Exhibit 10.

[36] NTIA, "NTIA Announces Availability of $121.5 Million in State Grants to Assist with
FirstNet Planning," February 6, 2013 (http://www.ntia.doc.gov/press-release/2013/ntia-
announces-availability-1215-million-state-grants-assistfirstnet-planning) and "State and
Local Implementation Grant Program Federal Funding Opportunity," February 6, 2013
(http://www.ntia.doc.gov/other-publication/2013/sligp-federal-funding-opportunity).

[37] NTIA Press release, "More than $116 Million Awarded to Assist States in FirstNet Planning," September   26,   2013,   http://www.ntia.doc.gov/press-release/2013/more-116-million-awarded-assist-states-firstnet-planning.

[38] NTIA, SLIGP Awards, http://www.ntia.doc.gov/sligp/sligp-awards.

[39] Current information on FirstNet's activities, including network design and state planning, is available at http://www.firstnet.gov.

[40] For examples, see CRS Report RS22230, Congressional or Federal Charters: Overview and Enduring Issues, by Kevin R. Kosar.

[41] P.L. 112-96, Section 6206 (a) (1).

[42] P.L. 112-96, Section 6206 (f).

[43] P.L. 112-96, Section 6208.

[44] P.L. 112-96, Section 6206 (b) (1).

[45] P.L. 112-96, Section 6205 (b) (1).

[46] Hearing, House Committee on Energy and Commerce, Subcommittee on Communications and Technology, "Oversight of FirstNet and the Advancement of Public Safety Wireless Communications," testimony of Samuel Ginn, Chairman, FirstNet, November 21, 2013.

[47] P.L. 112-96, Section 6204.

[48] Announcement and background information at http://www.ntia.doc.gov/other-publication/2012/acting-secretaryrebecca-blank-announces-board-directors-first-responder-netw.

[49] P.L. 112-96, Section 6206 (c) (1).

[50] P.L. 112-96, Section 6206 (c) (2).

[51] P.L. 112-96, Section 6206 (c) (3).

[52] P.L. 112-96, Section 6206 (c) (4).

[53] P.L. 112-96, Section 6206 (c) (5).

[54] P.L. 112-96, Section 6206 (c) (7).

[55] P.L. 112-96, Section 6205 (a).

[56] Board Resolution 1, By-Laws, http://www.ntia.doc.gov/files/ntia/publications/ firstnet_ reso lution_no._1_on_bylaws_adopted_9.25.12.pdf.

[57] NTIA, "FirstNet Names members of Public Safety Advisory Committee," February 20, 2013, http://www.ntia.doc.gov/press-release/2013/firstnet-names-members-public-safety-advisory-committee.

[58] See "Statewide Interoperability Coordinators" at http://www.dhs.gov/files/programs/ gc_ 1286986920144.shtm.

[59] P.L. 112-96, Section 6206 (c) (2) (B).

[60] P.L. 112-96, Section 6302 (d).

[61] Hearing, House Committee on Energy and Commerce, Subcommittee on Communications and Technology, "Oversight of FirstNet and the Advancement of Public Safety Wireless Communications," testimony of Samuel Ginn, Chairman, FirstNet, November 21, 2013. List of state contacts at http://firstnet.gov/sites/default/files/ SPOC_list_03102014.pdf.

[62] P.L. 112-96, Section 6302 (e) (1).

[63] P.L. 112-96, Section 6302 (e) (2) and (3).

[64] P.L. 112-96, Section 6302 (e) (3) (C) (iv).

[65] P.L. 112-96, Section 6302 (e) (3) (D).

[66] P.L. 112-96, Section 6302 (f).

[67] P.L. 112-96, Section 6302 (g).

[68] Small cells are low-powered radio access nodes that are used to boost capacity and manage network interference and connectivity. They can support LTE cellular networks in

configurations that include or emulate unlicensed WiFi standards for Wide Area Networks (WAN).

[69] P.L. 112-96, Section 6204.

[70] P.L. 112-96, Section 6302 (a).

[71] P.L. 112-96, Section 6302 (e) (3) (C) (iii) (I).

[72] P.L. 112-96, Section 6302 (e) (1) (C).

[73] P.L. 112-96, Section 6302 (e) (3) (C) (iii) (II).

[74] P.L. 112-96, Section 6201 (b).

[75] P.L. 112-96, Section 6206 (g).

[76] P.L. 112-96, Section 6208 (c).

[77] P.L. 112-96, Section 6209.

[78] P.L. 112-96, Section 6210.

[79] P.L. 112-96, Section 6001 (3).

[80] "Smart Grid" is the name given to the evolving electric power network as new information technology systems and capabilities are incorporated. See also CRS Report R41886, The Smart Grid and Cybersecurity—Regulatory Policy and Issues, by Richard J. Campbell.

[81] P.L. 112-96, Section 6206 (b) (1) (B).

[82] P.L. 112-96, Section 6206 (b) (1) (C).

[83] P.L. 112-96, Section 6206 (b) (3).

[84] P.L. 112-96, Section 6202 (a).

[85] P.L. 112-96, Section 6202 (b).

[86] P.L. 112-96, Section 6206 (c) (3).

[87] P.L. 112-96, Section 6206 (b) (3).

[88] P.L. 112-96, Section 6206, (c) (1).

[89] P.L. 112-96, Section 6206, (c) (2).

[90] P.L. 112-96, Section 6302 (e) (1).

[91] P.L. 112-96, Section 6302, (e) (2).

[92] P.L. 112-96, Section 6302, (e) (3) (B).

[93] P.L. 112-96, Section 6302 (e) (3) (C) (i).

[94] P.L. 112-96, Section 6302, (e) (3) (C) (iii).

[95] P.L. 112-96, Section 6302, (e) (3) (D) (i) (III).

[96] P.L. 112-96, Section 6503, "Section 158 "(a).

[97] P.L. 112-96, Section 6503, "Section 158 "(b).

[98] P.L. 112-96, Section 6503, "Section 158 "(c).

[99] P.L. 112-96, Section 6505.

[100] P.L. 112-96, Section 6504.

[101] P.L. 112-96, Section 6509.

[102] P.L. 112-96, Section 6507.

[103] P.L. 112-96, Section 6508.

[104] P.L. 112-96, Section 6506.

[105] P.L. 112-96, Section 6206 (b) (2) (C).

[106] P.L. 112-96, Section 6203 (c) (2).

[107] Also known as 3GPP Release 10, see http://www.3gpp.org/LTE-Advanced.

[108] P.L. 112-96, Section 6202 (b).

[109] P.L. 112-96, Section 6206 (b) (2) (B).

[110] P.L. 112-96, Section 6203.

[111] P.L. 112-96, Section 6203 (c) (1).

[112] P.L. 112-96, Section 6203 (c) (2).

[113] P.L. 112-96, Section 6203 (c) (3).

[114] P.L. 112-96, Section 6302 (e) (3) (C).

[115] Recommended Minimum Technical Requirements to Ensure Nationwide Interoperability for the Nationwide Public Safety Broadband Network, prepared by the Technical Advisory Board for First Responder Interoperability, Final Report, May 22, 2012, at http://www.fcc.gov/document/recommendations-interoperability-board.

[116] P.L. 112-96, Section 6303 (a).

[117] P.L. 112-96, Section 6303 (b) (1 − 5).

[118] P.L. 112-96, Section 6206 (c) (6).

[119] Discussed in GAO report, Emergency Communications: Various Challenges Likely to Slow Implementation of a Public Safety Broadband Network, February 2012, GAO-12-343.

[120] In addition to assigning NTIA responsibilities to develop public safety broadband communications, the act also specifies the NTIA's responsibility to promote efficient use of spectrum by the federal government. P.L. 112-96, Section 6410.

[121] More information is available at the PSCR website at http://www.ntia.doc.gov/category/public-safety. PSCR activities were discussed in testimony by Mary H. Saunders, Director, Standards Coordination Office, NIST before the House Committee on Homeland Security, Subcommittees on Emergency Preparedness, Response, and Communications and Cybersecurity, Infrastructure Protection, and Security Technologies, "First Responder Technologies: Ensuring a Prioritized Approach for Homeland Security Research and Development," May 9, 2012.

[122] P.L. 112-96, Section 6401 (b).

[123] FCC Public Notice, "Winning Bidder Announced for Auction 96," DA 14-279, February 28, 2014, http://transition.fcc.gov/Daily_Releases/Daily_Business/2014/db0228/DA-14-279A1.pdf.

[124] The PSCR, for example, has changed its plans for testing public safety interoperability in response to provisions in the act, http://www.pscr.gov/about_pscr/press/broadband/pscr_to_focus_on_publicsafety_broadband_interoperability_tests_042012-mission_critical.pdf.

[125] FCC, Connecting America: The National Broadband Plan, http://www.broad band.gov/download-plan/.

[126] P.L. 112-96, Section 6211.

[127] P.L. 112-95, Section 6206 (c) (5).

[128] P.L. 112-96 Section 6211.

[129] FCC, "Promoting Interoperability in the 700 MHZ Commercial Spectrum," Notice of Proposed Rulemaking, WT Docket No. 12-69, released March 21, 2012.

[130] FCC, "Report and Order and Order of Proposed Modification," WT Docket No. 12-69, released October 29, 2013.

[131] Hearing, House Committee on Energy and Commerce, Subcommittee on Communications and Technology, "Oversight of FirstNet and the Advancement of Public Safety Wireless Communications," testimony of Samuel Ginn, November 21, 2013.

[132] Informations on FEMA's Regional Centers at http://www.fema.gov/regional-operations.

[133] Information at https://www.dhs.gov/emergency-communications-preparedness-center.

[134] 4G Americas, Meeting the 100X Challenge: The Need for Spectrum, Technology and Policy Innovation, October 2013, http://www.4gamericas.org/ documents/ 2013_4G% 20Americas%20Meeting%20the%201000x%20Challenge%2010%204%2013_FINAL.pdf.

[135] Hearing, House Committee on Energy and Commerce, Subcommittee on Communications and Technology, "Oversight of FirstNet and the Advancement of Public Safety Wireless Communications," testimony of Samuel Ginn, November 21, 2013.

[136] Hearing, House Committee on Energy and Commerce, Subcommittee on Communications and Technology, "Oversight of FirstNet and the Advancement of Public Safety Wireless Communications," Opening Statement of Chairman Walden, November 21, 2013.

[137] In a meeting with CRS on January 29, 2014, NTIA officials noted that FirstNet is within the Department of Commerce, justifying steps such as the inclusion of "Department of Commerce" with the FirstNet logo, and repeatedly asserted that NTIA was in charge of FirstNet because it was the NTIA that would be held responsible by Congress for FirstNet's success or failure. The NTIA has created an Office of Public Safety Communications specifically to administer the public safety responsibilities outlined to the NTIA in the act, including the administration of grants, among other responsibilities.

[138] The term has been used, for example, by Rear Admiral (ret.) Jamie Barnett, former head of the FCC's Public Safety and Homeland Security Bureau, in discussions of FirstNet.

[139] See CRS Report R42889, Issues in the Reauthorization of Amtrak, by David Randall Peterman and John Frittelli.

[140] CRS Report 70-299 E, The Rail Passenger Service Act of 1970: Public Law 91-518, by Thomas E. McCardell, December 1, 1970. Available upon request from the author of this report.

[141] Ibid.

[142] Arnold Adams, "The National Railroad Passenger Corporation—A Modern Hybrid Corporation Neither Private nor Public," The Business Lawyer, Vol. 31, January 1976.

[143] Regional Rail Reorganization Act of 1973, House of Representatives Conference Report, No. 93-744, December 20, 1973.

[144] The Administrative Budget for FY2014 proposed privatizing the TVA and required the Office of Management and Budget to perform a strategic review.

[145] The Second Machine Age: Work, Progress and Prosperity in a Time of Brilliant Technologies, by Erik Byrnjolfsson and Andrew McAfee, W.W. Norton and Company Ltd., January 20, 2014.

[146] Paul Taylor, "AT&T Shifts to 'Virtualised' Hardware," Financial Times, February 26, 2014.

INDEX

#

21st century, 70
9/11, 73, 74, 116, 129, 157
9/11 Commission, 73, 74, 116, 129, 157

A

access, viii, 8, 10, 15, 16, 18, 28, 38, 41, 46, 63, 69, 114, 116, 118, 121, 128, 133, 134, 135, 137, 138, 139, 140, 141, 142, 143, 144, 147, 148, 149, 150, 151, 159
accounting, 41
accreditation, 64
administrators, 154
advancements, 15, 51, 58, 61
aerospace, 93
appointments, 136
appropriations, vii, 127, 154
Appropriations Act, 73, 123
assessment, 27, 32, 54, 55, 56, 64, 66, 68, 80, 83, 84, 99, 104, 110
assets, 3, 12, 31, 51, 52, 53, 55, 56, 88, 89, 106, 107, 108, 109, 114, 119, 124, 126, 131, 155, 157
AT&T, 157, 162
Attorney General, 75, 136, 140
audit(s), 134, 141, 155
authentication, 55, 148

authorities, 21, 72, 73, 75, 88, 90, 115, 118, 120, 130, 135, 145
authority, 38, 72, 116, 117, 124, 131, 134, 136, 139, 141, 145, 150, 156, 157
awareness, 3, 4, 15, 16, 19, 21, 22, 46, 47, 48, 49, 52, 64, 68, 117

B

background information, 159
bandwidth, 16, 17, 18, 62
bandwidth allocation, 17
bankruptcy, 155
barriers, viii, 128, 146
base, 31, 38, 88, 135, 139, 142
batteries, 56
benchmarks, 5, 24, 66, 67, 71, 96
benefits, 16, 23, 28, 42, 45, 59, 61, 139, 152
blueprint, 64
board members, 147, 151
bonds, 156
Broadband, 5, 6, 9, 11, 16, 17, 18, 19, 23, 27, 31, 38, 39, 55, 58, 60, 62, 63, 75, 86, 90, 104, 110, 114, 118, 124, 157, 161
broadband network, vii, viii, 4, 16, 19, 22, 63, 116, 127, 128, 130, 131, 132, 134, 135, 136, 137, 138, 139, 140, 142, 143, 144, 146, 147, 148, 149, 150, 153, 154, 158
building blocks, 113

business partners, 142
businesses, 157

C

call centers, 52, 115, 145
capital expenditure, 157
casting, 59
certification, 43, 83
challenges, vii, viii, 8, 11, 17, 18, 23, 25, 27, 28, 43, 44, 45, 51, 59, 68, 87, 94, 99, 128
changing environment, 10
Chicago, 158
Chief of Staff, 151
City, 124
civil liberties, 15
clarity, 31
Coast Guard, 88
coherence, viii, 128
collaboration, 1, 4, 26, 27, 28, 29, 32, 59, 60, 66, 69, 92, 123
commerce, 119, 122
commercial, viii, 12, 16, 17, 18, 19, 21, 40, 42, 51, 55, 58, 61, 62, 63, 89, 117, 128, 129, 130, 133, 137, 138, 139, 142, 143, 147, 148, 150, 151
communication, 3, 18, 24, 36, 44, 52, 61, 88, 90, 91, 107, 109, 114, 115
Communications Act, 72, 73, 119
Communications Act of 1934, 72, 119
communications lines, viii, 128
communities, 4, 6, 8, 18, 21, 60, 85, 123
community, vii, 2, 3, 6, 7, 8, 10, 11, 13, 15, 16, 17, 18, 23, 24, 25, 27, 28, 34, 36, 41, 44, 47, 49, 59, 60, 61, 62, 63, 64, 66, 68, 69, 70, 77, 78, 81, 85, 91, 96, 102, 103, 106, 110, 121, 122, 123
community support, 23
compatibility, 130, 151
competition, 142, 147
competitiveness, 151
complexity, 18, 83, 116, 118
compliance, 33, 64, 122
composition, 137, 142
computer, 56

Conference Report, 162
confidentiality, 15, 18, 115, 123
configuration, 139
conformity, 104
congress, v, vii, viii, 69, 83, 108, 109, 125, 126, 127, 128, 129, 131, 134, 136, 140, 141, 142, 143, 145, 150, 152, 153, 154, 155, 156, 157, 158, 162
connectivity, 16, 17, 129, 159
consensus, 70, 96
consolidation, 32
construction, viii, 128, 134, 135, 137, 138, 142, 144
consulting, 135
consumers, 134, 147
convention, 115
convergence, 16
cooperation, 28, 54, 66
cooperative agreements, 32, 124
correlation(s), 43, 68
cost, viii, 28, 33, 41, 46, 58, 128, 133, 134, 138, 153, 158
cost saving, 28, 33
covering, 83, 99
crises, 56
critical infrastructure, 10, 15, 20, 21, 75, 77, 84, 89, 92, 123
curricula, 44
curriculum, 46, 104, 112
customers, 151
cybersecurity, 4, 10, 29, 40, 59, 61, 75, 123
cycles, 157

D

data center, 143, 152
data collection, 135
data communication, 55, 117
database, 117
deficit, 133
demonstrations, 97
Department of Commerce, 58, 125, 131, 154, 162
Department of Defense, 60, 106, 125

Department of Homeland Security, v, 1, 5, 8, 72, 73, 76, 82, 90, 94, 95, 97, 105, 110, 122, 123, 129, 131, 136, 137, 140, 157
Department of Justice, 148, 149
Department of the Interior, 88
Department of Transportation, 107
deployments, 2, 27, 29, 37, 40, 50, 152, 153
deposits, 149
destruction, 114
digital technologies, 145
digital television, 132
directives, 75
directors, 154, 159
disaster, vii, 17, 40, 51, 73, 87, 90, 105, 115, 125, 127
disaster area, 40, 105
disaster relief, 90
distance learning, 47
distribution, 15, 89, 135
DOC, 108
drawing, 94

E

earthquakes, 8, 99
economies of scale, 39, 130, 139
ecosystem, 18, 19, 55, 69, 70, 84
education, 18, 80, 135
educational institutions, 119, 122
educational materials, 48
Emergency Assistance, 73, 74
emergency management, 6, 18, 27, 28, 30, 50, 52, 55, 56, 85, 86, 115, 116, 119, 122, 124
emergency medical services, vii, 8, 11, 54, 115, 121
emergency personnel, vii, 127, 145
emergency preparedness, 2, 31, 73, 77, 93, 116, 121, 122
emergency responder, vii, 2, 4, 5, 6, 7, 8, 9, 10, 11, 13, 14, 16, 21, 22, 25, 34, 40, 42, 43, 44, 46, 48, 57, 59, 60, 62, 66, 69, 70, 74, 75, 80, 84, 85, 94, 104, 117, 118, 121, 124

employees, 151
energy, 84, 130, 131
enforcement, 151
enrollment, 87
environment(s), 1, 2, 5, 6, 8, 10, 13, 15, 16, 17, 19, 27, 28, 34, 35, 36, 44, 51, 58, 62, 68, 69, 77, 85, 110, 113, 115, 118, 146, 153
Environmental Protection Agency, 88
equipment, 33, 40, 42, 43, 48, 50, 54, 58, 64, 69, 70, 80, 96, 112, 113, 114, 115, 116, 117, 119, 121, 142, 143, 148, 152, 154
evacuation, 19
evidence, 85, 114
evolution, 4, 58, 59, 62, 64, 107, 109, 117, 118, 125
execution, 41, 46, 51, 72, 91
executive branch, 118
Executive Order(s), 75, 76, 77, 93, 122, 124
exercise, 2, 3, 7, 42, 43, 44, 45, 46, 47, 48, 54, 80, 125, 136
exercise programs, 2, 3, 7, 42, 43, 44, 45, 46, 80
expenditures, 134, 136, 137, 139, 141
expertise, 90, 91, 94, 125, 136
exploitation, 115, 123
extreme weather events, 10

F

faith, 118, 122
family members, 21
federal agency, 136
Federal Communications Commission, 21, 70, 72, 74, 121, 122, 130, 145
Federal Emergency Management Agency, 26, 73, 102, 106, 122, 126, 153
federal facilities, 146
Federal Government, 31, 32, 34, 36, 62, 68, 72, 73, 75, 76, 77, 84, 85, 87, 88, 92, 93, 115, 118, 122, 136, 149, 154, 155, 156, 161
federal hiring, viii, 128

FEMA, 26, 30, 35, 48, 51, 94, 102, 103, 104, 105, 106, 107, 109, 122, 125, 126, 161
fiber, 142
fidelity, 157
financial, 28, 32, 90, 103, 124, 141, 154
financial condition, 141
financial support, 154
fires, 88
first responders, vii, 80, 85, 88, 127, 129, 130, 151
FirstNet, v, vii, viii, 127, 128, 130, 131, 132, 133, 134, 135, 136, 137, 138, 139, 140, 141, 142, 143, 144, 146, 147, 148, 150, 151, 152, 153, 154, 155, 156, 157, 158, 159, 161, 162
flexibility, 145
floods, 19, 99
food, 90, 118, 122
force, 113
formation, 154
funding, viii, 2, 17, 34, 75, 88, 97, 105, 112, 117, 128, 133, 135, 136, 138, 139, 140, 141, 144, 146, 149, 153, 155, 156, 158
funds, vii, viii, 127, 128, 133, 135, 139, 141, 146, 149

G

GAO, 141, 143, 146, 156, 157, 161
General Services Administration, 146
governance, viii, 1, 3, 6, 10, 12, 17, 23, 24, 25, 26, 27, 28, 29, 32, 34, 47, 67, 69, 95, 106, 120, 128, 140, 152, 153, 154, 155, 156, 157
governments, 6, 11, 24, 27, 32, 34, 47, 48, 70, 71, 76, 87, 92, 115, 118
governor, 138, 144
grant programs, 2, 32, 33, 74, 103, 152
grants, 26, 31, 32, 34, 93, 124, 132, 133, 134, 135, 138, 140, 141, 145, 158, 162
growth, 27, 62
guidance, 11, 26, 29, 32, 33, 36, 45, 68, 69, 76, 82, 85, 88, 92, 94, 100, 103, 105, 116, 124, 141

guidelines, viii, 41, 123, 128, 137

H

hazardous materials, 88
hazards, 7, 8, 10, 17, 23, 69, 73, 81
health, 84, 90, 119
hiring, 136, 151
history, 89
Homeland Security Act, 4, 5, 8, 24, 60, 72, 73, 74, 116, 119, 122, 124, 126, 137
House, 71, 109, 141, 157, 159, 161, 162
House of Representatives, 109, 162
human, viii, 8, 128
human resources, viii, 128
hurricanes, 8, 10, 19, 99
hybrid, 156

I

identification, 52, 80, 83, 111, 116, 146
images, 17, 19, 114, 131
improvements, 5, 23, 68, 72, 113, 145
income, 156
individuals, 15, 19, 21, 27, 40, 52, 63, 73, 75, 85, 86, 120, 126
industry, 41, 61, 103, 104, 119, 122, 123, 138, 142, 151, 155
information exchange, 19, 27, 36, 55, 92
information sharing, 1, 16, 21, 23, 26, 30, 32, 44, 45, 79, 85, 90, 116, 122, 124
information technology, 1, 11, 27, 29, 36, 40, 56, 61, 87, 93, 126, 160
infrastructure, viii, 2, 10, 16, 17, 19, 21, 28, 32, 38, 39, 41, 57, 58, 60, 71, 77, 84, 89, 90, 108, 114, 123, 124, 128, 131, 133, 134, 137, 139, 142, 143, 145, 147, 149, 152, 153, 156
Integrated Public Alert and Warning System, 20, 58, 104
integration, 4, 6, 11, 23, 24, 38, 59, 62, 68, 69, 82, 146, 153
integrity, 15, 17, 18, 115, 123
intellectual property, 60

Intelligence Reform and Terrorism
    Prevention Act, 73
interagency coordination, 113, 115
interface, 62, 113
interference, 132, 159
investment(s), viii, 2, 9, 10, 17, 23, 25, 26,
    27, 30, 32, 33, 35, 59, 60, 97, 120, 128,
    135, 139, 140, 149, 151, 153, 156
islands, 87
issues, 10, 15, 24, 26, 27, 28, 30, 43, 55, 59,
    60, 62, 92, 93, 112, 124, 157

J

judicial branch, 118
jurisdiction(s), 17, 41, 67, 80, 85, 88, 117,
    129, 141

L

land mobile radio systems, 119
landscape, vii, 5, 13, 14, 16, 23, 27, 92
large-scale disasters, 31, 50
law enforcement, vii, 8, 11, 15, 54, 85, 90,
    115, 117, 121
laws, vii, viii, 127, 128, 129, 145
lead, 2, 8, 12, 38, 58, 152, 157
leadership, 1, 6, 12, 24, 28, 29, 31, 93, 111,
    120, 126
legislation, 5, 8, 87, 155
light, 10, 157
loan guarantees, 154
loans, 32, 124, 154
local authorities, 137
local government, 73, 115, 119, 123, 137,
    145
logistics, 54
Louisiana, 108, 135

M

magnitude, 8
major issues, 113
majority, 24, 55, 79, 89

malware, 18
man, 8, 16, 70, 71, 85
management, 15, 17, 62, 66, 72, 73, 75, 76,
    80, 82, 83, 85, 109, 115, 116, 136, 139,
    140, 151, 152, 153, 154, 156, 157
man-made disasters, 70, 71
marketplace, 4, 59, 61, 62
Maryland, 124
materials, 33, 117
matrix, 122
matter, 86, 91, 120
measurement(s), 66, 68, 114, 126
media, 15, 17, 19, 20, 21, 36, 41, 45, 62, 92,
    106
medical, vii, 8, 11, 15, 17, 41, 54, 85, 114,
    115, 117, 121
membership, 30, 94, 102, 112, 125
membership criteria, 102
messages, 21, 63
methodology, 39, 79, 125
metropolitan areas, 97, 98
Mexico, 48
Miami, 158
Middle Class Tax Relief and Job Creation
    Act, vii, 119, 124, 125, 127, 129, 149
migration, 90, 146, 148
military, 88, 117
miscommunication, 51
mission(s), 4, 5, 7, 8, 11, 13, 14, 16, 18, 23,
    24, 34, 35, 40, 42, 49, 54, 55, 57, 59, 61,
    64, 69, 70, 77, 79, 82, 84, 85, 86, 91, 92,
    104, 118, 119, 120, 121, 122, 139, 148,
    152, 161
Missouri, 50, 106
mobile communication, 55, 128
mobile device, 17, 59, 60, 113, 153
mobile phone, 19
modernization, 18, 23, 32, 154
modifications, 151

N

naming, 115
National Broadband Plan, 150, 161
national emergency, 76, 91, 126

national policy, 75, 76
National Response Framework, 44, 45, 52, 54, 76, 81, 82, 96, 107, 118, 119, 122, 126
National Response Plan, 76
national security, 2, 4, 31, 60, 72, 77, 93, 116, 121, 122, 124
national strategy, 124
nationwide network, viii, 124, 128, 129, 133, 134, 135, 138, 139, 152, 153
natural disaster(s), 8, 10, 30, 70, 71, 99, 118
natural gas, 74
NECP, vii
negotiating, viii, 128
networking, 153
neutral, 59
next generation, 58, 70, 147, 149
nodes, 139, 142, 159
nonprofit organizations, 73, 118, 122

O

obstacles, 24, 71
Office of Management and Budget, 75, 136, 140, 162
officials, 6, 11, 12, 18, 25, 37, 42, 44, 50, 58, 62, 70, 80, 85, 90, 91, 94, 105, 121, 125, 126, 129, 162
oil, 88
Oklahoma, 50
operating costs, 147
opportunities, 2, 3, 27, 32, 42, 44, 45, 46, 47, 48, 62, 69, 116, 152
opt out, 141, 144
organize, 115, 116
outreach, 6, 7, 11, 30, 38, 47, 68, 125, 135, 151
oversight, 29, 43, 134, 140, 141, 156
overtime, 44

P

parallel, 38, 128
participants, 72, 113, 125, 135, 138

partnerships, viii, 4, 7, 9, 27, 28, 30, 34, 49, 50, 60, 62, 84, 87, 92, 119, 122, 124, 128, 133, 134, 139, 140, 142, 152, 153, 155, 156
penalties, 146
permit, 125, 151
Philadelphia, 124, 158
police, 17, 115, 153
policy, viii, 5, 9, 26, 28, 31, 82, 92, 93, 94, 95, 124, 128, 129, 132, 154
policy initiative, viii, 128
policy makers, viii, 95, 128, 129, 132, 154
portfolio, 78, 152
potential benefits, 21, 139
preparation, 4, 38, 47, 57, 69, 76, 78, 136, 144, 145
preparedness, 8, 10, 15, 30, 31, 57, 75, 76, 77, 78, 81, 85, 89, 91, 96, 107, 113, 121, 122, 125, 161
pre-planning, 54
preservation, 85
president, 31, 72, 74, 76, 78, 93, 110, 141, 154
Presidential Directives, 76
prevention, 115, 123
primary function, 19
principles, 51, 82, 83, 123, 153
private sector, viii, 5, 6, 10, 11, 19, 21, 25, 36, 44, 50, 52, 53, 54, 59, 63, 66, 70, 76, 83, 84, 87, 89, 90, 92, 93, 102, 118, 119, 122, 123, 125, 128, 130, 135, 140, 142, 149, 155, 156
probability, 116, 121
procurement, 27, 33, 87, 136, 152
professionals, 114
profit, 74, 90, 154, 155
programming, 125
project, 34, 104, 143, 144
propagation, 59
protection, 85, 108, 115, 123, 132
public health, vii, 11, 15, 41, 114, 117
public interest, 72, 150
public officials, 85
public sector, viii, 3, 45, 128
public service, 155

public support, 112
public works, vii, 11, 42, 117
public-private partnerships, 50, 119, 122, 134, 155

Q

Quadrennial Homeland Security Review, 10, 72, 122, 126
qualifications, 83
quality of service, 145

R

radio, vii, 16, 21, 25, 28, 40, 45, 53, 56, 72, 82, 91, 105, 113, 114, 117, 118, 125, 127, 132, 134, 135, 138, 139, 140, 141, 142, 143, 144, 148, 150, 157, 159
real time, 113
recognition, 48, 64
recommendations, 7, 12, 13, 24, 28, 32, 33, 36, 45, 52, 59, 64, 65, 68, 69, 70, 71, 73, 74, 79, 80, 82, 92, 93, 94, 97, 105, 107, 108, 113, 125, 129, 141, 147, 156, 157, 161
recovery, viii, 7, 11, 15, 17, 20, 21, 28, 32, 40, 41, 42, 49, 58, 67, 73, 76, 89, 90, 115, 128, 129, 153
redundancy, 16, 119
reform, 73
regulations, 154
reimburse, 133
reliability, 16, 18, 69, 89, 92
remediation, 69
Reorganization Act, 155, 162
research facilities, 4, 61, 62
reserves, 53
resilience, 8, 10, 31, 55, 75, 76, 77, 78, 145
resource allocation, 79, 80, 125
resource management, 115
restoration, 21, 41, 89, 115, 123
revenue, vii, viii, 127, 128, 133, 134, 138, 139, 146, 149
rights, 87, 116

risk(s), 10, 18, 40, 51, 62, 76, 78, 79, 80, 97, 115, 123, 139
risk assessment, 80
rules, 74, 150
rural areas, 59, 87, 151

S

saving lives, 19
scope, 8, 44, 99, 143, 149
Secretary of Commerce, 75, 136, 140, 141
Secretary of Homeland Security, 73, 74, 75, 76, 137
secure communication, 85
security, 2, 8, 15, 16, 18, 27, 29, 31, 35, 37, 40, 55, 58, 60, 61, 62, 64, 69, 72, 76, 77, 78, 80, 87, 92, 106, 114, 122, 126, 137, 138, 152
Senate, 109, 141
sensors, 17
September 11, vii, 127, 129
service provider, 12, 53, 58, 62, 63, 74, 93, 142
shape, 15, 69, 92, 105
shareholders, 154
shelter, 90
signals, 131
signs, 17
small businesses, 119, 122
small communities, 8
software, 17, 142
solution, vii, 4, 62, 95, 96, 127, 150
sovereignty, 87
specialists, 125
specifications, 104, 146
Spectrum Act, viii, 128, 129, 130, 131, 133, 135, 140, 142, 143, 145, 147, 150, 153, 155
staffing, 4, 56
Stafford Act, 73
stakeholders, 3, 5, 6, 7, 10, 11, 14, 19, 25, 30, 36, 45, 55, 65, 66, 67, 68, 69, 79, 84, 92, 104, 105, 110, 125, 129, 136, 142, 144, 145, 155